SYNAPTIC

TRANSMISSION

HUGH McLENNAN, Ph.D.

Associate Professor of Physiology,
Faculty of Medicine, The University of
British Columbia, Vancouver, Canada

W. B. SAUNDERS COMPANY

Philadelphia · London, 1963

To

SIR LINDOR BROWN, C.B.E., F.R.S.,

Waynflete Professor of Physiology in the University
of Oxford
this book is dedicated with respect
and affection.

PREFACE

This work is concerned specifically with the details of synaptic transmission processes, having regard to the three main areas in which experimental investigations have been undertaken. These are: the morphology of synaptic regions; the electrical consequences of synaptic activation; and the nature of the chemical transmitter substances involved. Although the most intensive treatment is of events taking place in the mammalian central nervous system, I have discussed also synapses in other sites and organisms in an attempt to demonstrate the very considerable areas of qualitative similarity which exist between these various situations. The coverage is not intended to be exhaustive, sufficient detail having been introduced to demonstrate the considerable flexibility of synaptic interaction which underlies the extraordinary complexity of function inherent in all nervous systems.

It is a pleasure to acknowledge my indebtedness to my colleagues in Vancouver and elsewhere for much helpful discussion, and to many others around the world who have kindly permitted me to reproduce illustrations from their published works. Reference to these authors is made in the captions to the figures. I wish also especially to thank my colleague Dr. Patricia Emmons for her help in preparing the index and for checking the proofs; and my assistant and secretary Miss Mary-Jo Cullen for her untiring efforts on my behalf.

Finally, it is with gratitude that I acknowledge the generous financial assistance granted to me by the Muscular Dystrophy Association of Canada, without which this work could not have been undertaken.

H. McLennan

Vancouver, B.C.

CONTENTS

INTRODUCTION

It is only some 70 years since the term "neurone" was introduced by Waldeyer (1891) to describe the nerve cell as a single entity separate from but intermingled among its neighbors; the term included the nucleated cell body and all of its processes.* This definition was in fact the enunciation of the theory of the function of neurones as independent units. The theory marks the beginning of the understanding of the operations of the nervous system, and is now so much a commonplace that it is difficult to reconstruct the arguments which its expression raised among histologists at the turn of this century. The silver-staining methods devised by Golgi and their employment, especially by Cajal, dealt a death blow to the preceding prevalent hypothesis of continuity between the processes of contiguous nerve cells and of the propagation of nervous impulses through the network formed by their intermingled dendrites. The new discoveries demonstrated that in fact there was no such continuity between adjacent cell processes, while at the same time points of contact were recognized.

To such a point of contact between neuronal processes, the name "synapsis" was given by Sherrington (1897), and it is with the details of the operation of junctions between nerve cells and between neurones and effector cells that this present work is concerned. The fundamental importance of the synaptic linkages between cells was early recognized, as the following quotation will serve to illustrate

* "Das Nervensystem besteht aus zahlreichen untereinander anatomisch wie genetisch nicht zusammenhängenden Nervenheiten (Neuronen). Jede Nervenheit setzt sich zusammen aus drei Stücken, der Nervenzelle, der Nervenfaser und dem Faserbäumchen (Endbäumchen)."

(Schäfer, 1900): "On the other hand a path which includes any of the higher nerve centres or any complex nerve processes, must have a chain of several cells with a synapse at the place of contact between each two links in the chain. There is reason to believe that the additional delay (lost time) which is characteristic of the passage of nervous impulses through the nerve centres is due to a block at each synapse, that in fact the nervous impulses are momentarily arrested at these places of contact of the nerve cells with one another, and it is not improbable that the relative number of these blocks will furnish a key to the differences which are found to obtain in the reaction time for different reflexes and psychical processes."

Following on from these findings much early work was performed which foreshadowed in remarkable degree the results which will be discussed in greater detail later in this book. For example, it was found, as implied in the above quotation, that each synapse in a nervous pathway imposed a delay upon the passage of an impulse, and further that the delays at different synapses were probably roughly of the same magnitude. Thus, Wundt in 1871 reported that the minimal delay for contraction of the frog's gastrocnemius muscle following stimulation of a posterior root was 8 msec., while for a crossed extensor reflex after the same stimulation the latency was 12 msec. When recognition of the existence of synapses had been made, the conclusion was correctly drawn that the second reflex involved more such connections, and it was suggested that the delay at each was about 2 msec. In 1910 Jolly also measured synaptic delays of about 2 msec. and further concluded from his measurements that the knee-jerk reflex involved only a single synapse in the spinal cord, while simple flexor reflexes were disynaptic. When one considers the techniques which had to be used to make these measurements, their accuracy is worthy of remark and admiration.

Among the many other early investigations of the function of excitable tissues which underlie the advances to be described here are those which relate to the polarization of the cells. The author who earliest stated the matter definitively was duBois-Reymond in 1849 (duBois-Reymond, 1860), who demonstrated that a persistent voltage could be detected in all nerves at rest; and Bernstein (1868) claimed that in the resting state a nerve or muscle fiber had an excess of positive ions on the outside and negative on the inside, ascribing this situation to a selective permeability of the cellular membrane to potassium ions.

The discovery of the action potentials of excitable tissues is also often ascribed to duBois-Reymond, although the honor in fact belongs to Matteucci (1842), who some years earlier had demonstrated the reduction in the steady potential between the cut end of a muscle and its intact surface during tetanic activity, a process which we would now recognize as due to the repetitive depolarization of the fibers. Although analysis of the details of the action potential had to await the introduction of the cathode ray oscilloscope, first used by Gasser and Erlanger (1922), yet before its development the discontinuous nature of the electrical signs of activity was recognized and accepted before the end of the nineteenth century. Finally, the all-or-nothing nature of the conducted action potential of nerve was established by Adrian (1912) in the early years of this century.

I have felt it justified to introduce this book by mentioning, albeit briefly, the discoveries of some of the founders of neurophysiology, and more specifically, of those whose efforts laid the basis for the knowledge of synaptic transmission processes which we now possess. We must recognize above all others the contributions made by the brilliant and detailed work of Sherrington, whose *The Integrative Action of the Nervous System* (1906 and subsequent editions) yet remains a source of inspiration for all whose interest lies in this direction.

Chapter 2

THE MORPHOLOGY OF SYNAPSES

After recognition of the facts that neurones were anatomically distinct units and that there was no physical continuity between their processes, Held (1897) demonstrated the existence of swellings at the ends of axons which could be seen to be applied to the somata and dendrites of other cells. These swellings, to which various names have been given—"boutons terminaux," "end-bulbs," "end-feet," etc. —are now recognized as one, and perhaps the principal, type of synaptic contact linking the neurones in functional chains.

SYNAPSES AT MAMMALIAN MOTONEURONES

The surface of the soma and of the proximal portions of the dendrites of a typical motoneurone of the mammalian spinal cord is thickly covered with synaptic boutons, and the only region which is comparatively free from such endings is the conical portion of the soma from which the axon emerges (the axon hillock). Wyckoff and Young (1956) have estimated that probably four-fifths of the surface area is thus occupied, and that the total number of such contacts upon a single cell may be upwards of 2000. The greater number of the endings are 1 to 2 μ in diameter, but some are found as large as 5 μ. There is no evidence of an orderly arrangement of the varying sizes of boutons, large and small apparently being distributed randomly across the cell surface.

The development of the electron microscope has been of tremendous value in the acquisition of knowledge of the fine structures of these endings, for it is only with the aid of this instrument that sufficient magnification is available to permit the study of single synapses. I have deliberately selected the motoneurone for discussion first, and the boutons upon it as examples of what may be called "typical" synapses, for much of our information on the physiology of synaptic action derives from these cells. A shorter discussion of the many other types of synapse which have been identified will be taken up later.

The first electron microscope studies date only from 1953, but intensive work in a number of laboratories has revealed submicroscopic features which are common to many synapses from a wide variety of animals. The following is a brief description of these general features. It is recognized that although the bouton is closely applied to the membrane of what we may now call the postsynaptic cell, there is no actual physical contact between the two. The intervening space is known as the "synaptic cleft," and separates the bounding membranes of the bouton and of the postsynaptic soma, dendrite, or axon. Its width varies from 100 to 500 Å, depending upon the source of material used for study: at mammalian motoneurones 200 Å is about the average value. It is usually stated that there is no intrusion of glial elements into the cleft, but this is not true in all instances (Birks, Huxley, and Katz, 1960; Birks, 1962); possible changes in the extent of this glial intrusion provide another parameter, which has so far been little considered in the mechanisms of synaptic action. It is clear however that the cleft is a free continuation of the interstitial spaces, i.e., that it is filled with the extracellular fluid with which the neurones are surrounded. It is, of course, well known that the total volume of the

3

extracellular space in the central nervous system is extremely small (de Robertis, 1962). The closeness of packing of the cells, both neural and non-neural, is such that the channels between them are rarely more than a few hundred Å wide, i.e., they are of the same order of size as the synaptic clefts. The true extracellular fluid of the brain is present only within these narrow channels.

The membranes that limit both bouton and that portion of the postsynaptic cell underlying the ending (which will henceforth be called the subsynaptic membrane) are not uniformly electron-dense. There are patches in each that show a greater density, and the denser areas tend to lie opposite one another. These are indicated in the drawing of a typical bouton shown in Figure 2.1. Within the bouton itself are seen many mitochondria and often a "tail" of neurofibrils, which extends into the ending and may there form a ring surrounding the mitochondria (Boycott, Gray, and Guillery, 1961). Also present in the cytoplasm of the bouton are numerous small (200 to 600 Å diameter) bodies which were named "synaptic vesicles" by de Robertis and Bennett (1954, 1955) and Palay (1954). These vesicles appear to be concentrated in the neighborhood of the membrane bounding the

synaptic cleft and in particular near those areas of greater electron density, and were originally described as roughly spherical in shape and independent of one another. As we shall see in later chapters, an elaborate correlation between structure and function of synapses has been based on this morphological picture; but it is necessary to point out at this early stage that the interpretation of the electron microscopic data has been questioned by Birks (1961, and Personal Communication). He has obtained evidence, from careful analysis of serial electron miscroscopic sections of frog neuromuscular junctions in which these "vesicles" are also seen, that the profiles are not compatible with their being simple spheres, and that they may in fact form part of a continuous tubular apparatus extending from the synaptic region through the ending and opening into the extracellular space between ending and glial cell. Although in the ensuing discussion the term "vesicle" will continue to be used, it should be realized that a modification of the currently accepted concepts may become necessary in the future. It was early recognized and is now firmly established that the vesicles are in the main characteristic of the presynaptic terminal, and are rarely, except in one specific case (to be discussed later), seen in the cytoplasm of the subsynaptic regions of the postsynaptic structure.

These then are the essential elements of a "typical" motoneuronal synapse—the bouton with its contained synaptic vesicles, the cleft bounded by membranes which, although of approximately uniform thickness (about 60 Å), are divided into zones of greater and lesser electron density, and the subsynaptic area of the postsynaptic cell. It should be recalled again that four-fifths of the motoneuronal surface may be occupied in this fashion.

There is evidence, however, that these typical synapses are likely not to be the only ones which act upon mammalian motoneurones, and furthermore that some distinction in function among the various sizes of boutons can be drawn. The motoneurones of the quadriceps muscle lie in the fifth and sixth lumbar segments of the spinal cord, and section of the corresponding sensory roots will lead to the degeneration of those synaptic endings which are the direct terminations of the posterior root fibers, i.e., those responsible for the monosynaptic stretch reflex arc. The number of such degenerating boutons is comparatively small, and they are among the largest endings

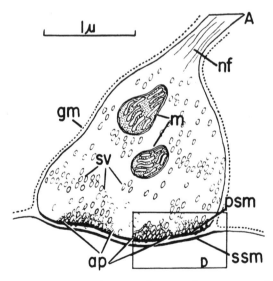

Figure 2.1. A drawing of a typical motoneuronal bouton, showing the characteristic submicroscopic features. Mitochondria (m), neurofibrils (nf), and synaptic vesicles (sv) are shown within the ending. The vesicles appear to be concentrated at regions (ap) of greater electron density of the presynaptic membrane (psm).

A.: axon; ssm.: subsynaptic membrane; gm.: glial membrane. (From de Robertis, 1959, by permission of Academic Press, Inc.)

impinging upon the motoneurone (Szentágo-thai, 1958). The greater number of boutons show no change and are therefore not involved in the monosynaptic activation of the cells.

In 1941 Renshaw first described the inhibition of spinal motoneurones brought about by antidromic stimulation of motor axons, a process which has been studied in greater detail by Eccles and his colleagues and will be discussed in Chapter 4. The anatomical pathway leading to this inhibition is now recognized as due to the existence of collateral branches of the motor axons which make synaptic contact with small cells lying in the region where the motor fibers are collected to leave the anterior horn of the cord. The axons of these small cells, which have been named "Renshaw cells," in turn form synapses with the motoneurones; and it has been shown that excitation of the Renshaw cells brings about synaptic inhibition of the motoneurones.

It is possible to isolate one anterior quadrant of the cord in such a way that only the peripheral part of the anterior horn remains viable, interference with the blood supply resulting in the destruction of other portions. Within this region only motoneurones and small cells which appear to be identifiable as Renshaw cells remain intact, and the only synapses upon the motoneurones must have originated from the Renshaw cells (Szentágo-thai, 1958). Only very occasionally was a typical bouton observed on the motoneurones in such preparations. On the other hand, many extremely fine fibers were found which had all the characteristics of terminal ramifications of axons. These formed intimate relationships with the somata and dendrites of the motoneurones, sometimes having the appearance of a fine meshwork closely enveloping the cell. Szentágothai has concluded from these observations that the inhibitory synapses upon a motoneurone which are activated by the Renshaw cells are not of the typical form. Upon the Renshaw cells themselves, however, typical boutons were seen, and since these cells are excited by impulses in the motor axons while they in turn inhibit the motoneurones, it is tempting to consider that excitatory and inhibitory synaptic contacts may have fundamentally different morphological configurations—the former typified by the boutons and the latter by diffuse networks of fine fibers possessing no specialized endings. This is little more than speculation at present, but it is important that we recognize the existence of types of contacts other than the circumscribed boutons which have been so extensively studied.

OTHER SYNAPSES BETWEEN NEURONES

The classic review of the various types of synapses recognized as occurring in the central nervous system is that of Cajal (1934), in which he divided the 11 described types into two broad groups, those in which the contact was with the cell body of the post-synaptic cell (axosomatic), and those upon the dendrites (axodendritic). In addition there have more recently been described synapses upon the axon (and particularly upon the axon hillock) of the postsynaptic cell, which may therefore be termed axo-axonic. These latter are particularly striking at some invertebrate neurones (see, e.g., Tauc, 1960b). It is unlikely that there is any fundamental difference in the mechanism of operation of individual synapses, whether they occur upon soma, dendrite or axon. It is however recognized that there are differences regarding the contribution which any given synapse can make to the electrical events in the postsynaptic cell as a whole which do depend upon the location of the synapses upon the cell (Fadgia and Brookhart, 1960).

The number of synaptic contacts formed by the endings of any given neurone depends, not unexpectedly, upon the complexity of the functions which it must carry out. In the simplest case, as that of many primary afferent neurones which may be regarded as typical bipolar cells, the axons may make only a single synaptic contact with the next neurone of the chain, and this synapse may be the only one impinging upon the postsynaptic cell. Such single endings may involve a considerable portion of the postsynaptic cell surface, and have been found, for example, in the tangential nucleus of goldfish. An example is shown in Figure 2.2. In higher centers of the vertebrate nervous system, the development of the dendritic processes of the neurones becomes much more complex (see, e.g., Horstmann, 1957); and the intermingling of the dendrites with the arborizations of the axons produces the dense neuropile of the higher grey areas of the brain. Within this the number of contacts per unit of volume must be immense, as has been emphasized by Bullock (1952) for the neuropiles of many invertebrate systems, where it is, in fact, found that

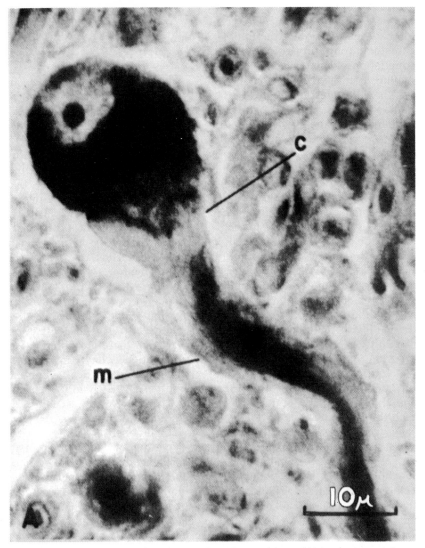

Figure 2.2. A neurone from the tangential nucleus of the goldfish, showing only a single large presynaptic ending upon it. *c,* The cup-like synaptic ending; *m,* the myelin sheath of the presynaptic axon. (From Bodian, 1952, by permission of the Long Island Biological Association, Inc.)

the somata of the cells are small and generally free from any synaptic junction. The contacts may be presumed to assume a considerable diversity of form, and it is further probable that there is functional significance both in the shape of the ending and in its location upon the processes of the postsynaptic neurone.

Mention has been made above of a probable functional distinction between the various types, sizes, and distribution of endings observable upon motoneurones. A more striking example of the same thing occurs at the giant Mauthner's neurones of some teleost fishes. Here the distal end of the large lateral dendrite receives only club-like endings of the axons of the eighth cranial nerve. More proximally there are typical large boutons which are present also upon the ventral dendrite. Upon the cell soma are found small club endings and a few boutons, while surrounding the axon hillock is a "spiral" synapse consisting of finely coiled fibers which have recently been shown to have an inhibitory function (see p. 67). A drawing of a typical Mauthner cell in the goldfish is given in Figure 2.3. It is quite clear in this case that synaptic endings

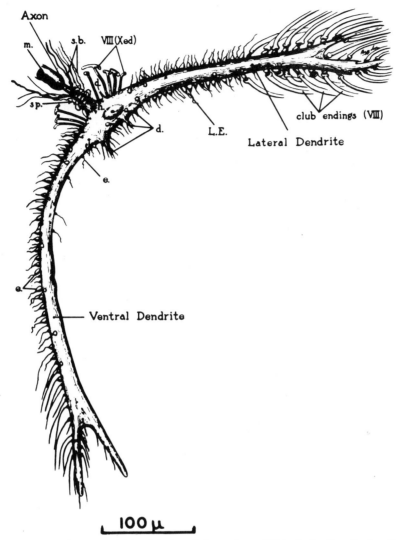

Figure 2.3. A drawing of Mauthner's cell from the goldfish, indicating the localization of different types of endings upon the postsynaptic neurone. *d*, Small dendrites; *e*, small end-bulbs; *h*, the axon hillock; *L.E.*, large end-bulbs; *m*, the myelin sheath of the axon; *s.b.*, the bundle giving rise to the "spiral" synapse; *sp.*, spiral fibers in the region of the axon hillock; *VIII(Xed)*, crossed vestibular fibers giving rise to collaterals, which terminate as small club endings; *VIII*, vestibular root fibers. (From Bodian, 1952, by permission of the Long Island Biological Association, Inc.)

emanating from various sources are not randomly distributed over the soma and dendrites of the postsynaptic cell, but are arranged in an orderly fashion such that those endings from one group of presynaptic neurones are localized to one portion of the cell. The precise functional significance of the localizations is not understood at the present time.

Cajal analyzed the distribution and type of synaptic contact existing upon the Purkinje cells of the cerebellum. Almost all the different types of synaptic endings known to occur in the central nervous system are found upon these cells, and Cajal was able to show not only that each type derived from a different afferent source, but further that their localization upon the processes of the postsynaptic cell was rigidly determined. Only upon the somata of the cells were to be found typical boutons, and these derived from axon collaterals of neighboring Purkinje neurones. The other endings were all of a more diffuse character, as for example those of the molecular layer, which form long filaments twining among the dendrites of the cells. Cajal himself remarked upon the atypical appearance of these synapses which, unfortunately, have not as yet been studied by electron microscopy.

The topographical localization of synapses upon frog motoneurones has similarly been described by Fadiga and Brookhart (1960). They have been able to show that volleys in the posterior roots and in the lateral columns lead to monosynaptic activation of the motoneurones, the former by contacts upon the distal parts of the dorsally directed dendrites, the latter upon the somata and more proximal dendritic regions. The lateral column connections are thus much more favorably placed for excitation of the neurones than are those of the sensory root fibers (see p. 30). In the mammalian spinal cord, Sprague (1958) has shown that posterior root fibers making ipsilateral monosynaptic connections with motoneurones terminate on the cell bodies and dorsal dendrites of the cells, whereas those from contralateral sources end only on the medial dendrites and never upon the somata. Again, the ipsilateral connections have the preferred position.

The constancy of these localizations is of very great interest and importance, not only for a complete understanding of the functions of the nervous system once the connections have been made, but as one likely contributing factor to the remarkable plasticity which it exhibits.

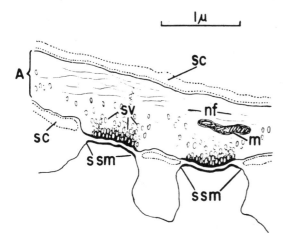

Figure 2.4. A drawing of a synapse "en passant" between an axon (*A*) and an electroplaque of the electric organ of an eel. The vesicles (*sv*) are concentrated at regions of greater electron density of the presynaptic and subsynaptic (*ssm*) membranes, and there is no intrusion of the Schwann cell (*sc*) into the synaptic cleft. *m*, Mitochondrion; *nf*, neurofibrils. (From de Robertis, 1959, by permission of Academic Press, Inc.)

As another example of "atypical" synapses, it is necessary to consider the lateral junctions which occur, for example, between axons and the electroplaques of certain fishes. Such synapses "en passant," shown diagrammatically in Figure 2.4, probably also have a wide distribution, and have been certainly identified in the cerebellum where the axons of the granule cells make contact with the dendrites of Purkinje neurones. It is evident from Figure 2.4 that the elements described for a typical bouton are present also in these situations. Thus, the axon shows a swelling in the region which adjoins the postsynaptic cell, and this enlargement has a high concentration of synaptic vesicles within it; the cleft which separates the two sides of the junction is about 500 Å wide; and the Schwann cell which envelops the axon throughout its length is absent from the synaptic area.

In summary it may be said that in the vertebrate central nervous system all synapses at which there is a distinct ending of the prejunctional axon exhibit similarities regardless of their source, although the differences in detail may well be of important functional significance. Thus, synapses in the spinal cord (Wyckoff and Young, 1956), the thalamus (Fernández-Morán, 1955), the cochlear nucleus (de Robertis, 1956), the cerebrum, cerebellum, and medulla (Palay, 1956), and the cerebral cortex (Gray, 1959; de Lorenzo, 1961) all have the features described above—objects appearing as vesicles in the presynaptic ending, areas of increased electron density and thickness (which may cover much or little of the synaptic membrane), and the cleft of a few hundred Å width separating the pre- from the postsynaptic surface. Interestingly, de Lorenzo (1961) has been able to demonstrate an histochemical difference between some axodendritic and the axosomatic synapses which both he and Gray (1959) described in the cerebral cortex. The former were found often to show dense staining for cholinesterase (in both pre- and postsynaptic membranes), while the latter did not. The possible significance of this finding is not certain, but is most interesting in the light of the functional localizations described by Fadiga and Brookhart (1960). Whether the finely coiled synapses which Szentágothai (1958) described upon motoneurones conform to these generalities as do the synapses "en passant" mentioned above has yet to be investigated, but it is at least conceivable that they may not.

NEUROMUSCULAR JUNCTIONS

Vertebrate Striated Muscle

The features of vertebrate neuromuscular junctions are in the main quite similar to those of the typical synapses between neurones, which we have discussed above, but because of their peripheral situation, their submicroscopic architecture is rather better known than is the case for structures of the central nervous system.

Light microscopy revealed that the motor axon, having lost its myelin sheath, divides and connects with the sarcoplasm. Within the branches, and especially in the underlying sarcoplasm, are many bodies which have the staining properties of mitochondria (and whose identity has been confirmed by electron microscopy). The branches of the nerve are surrounded by teloglia, and occupy troughs which are hollowed out in the sarcoplasm. These have been named "synaptic gutters." In transverse section the gutter is seen to be lined with lamellae which appear as rodlets less than 1 μ in length.

The finer structure of the synaptic gutters has become clear only through the use of the electron microscope. Within the fine axon terminals are seen many small vesicles, which are absent from the underlying sarcoplasm, but which may, as noted above, form part of a tubular reticulum. The nature of the lamellae lining the gutter has also been demonstrated. It is now known that they are formed from the membrane limiting the sarcoplasm, while the membrane bounding the terminal axon remains completely external to these infoldings. Robertson (1956) has observed that within the gap between the two membranes there are three layers, two outer ones which are comparatively less electron-dense, and a denser middle zone, all three layers of approximately the same thickness. The significance of these layers is not known. The general arrangement of a synaptic gutter is shown in Figure 2.5. The infolding of the sarcoplasm greatly enlarges the area of subsynaptic membrane present in each gutter and therefore may be expected to have a profound influence upon the operation of the synapse (see p. 22).

The arrangement of the folds within the gutter is complex and is different for various animal species. Couteaux (1958) has described the situation as follows:

"It is possible to show that the junctional folds are not digitate invaginations but long folds differently oriented in relation to the axis of the gutters containing the terminal nerve twigs (Figure 2.6).

"In the frog the folds are transverse and stretch from edge to edge of the gutter. This arrangement may be found in reptiles and in mammals, but it is much less frequent, and is only observed in general, along short gutter segments. In reptiles and in mammals the orientation of the folds often differs considerably according to whether we are dealing with the deep part of the gutter or the regions neighbouring the edges. In the deep part of the gutter, the folds may be orientated in different patterns and often lon-

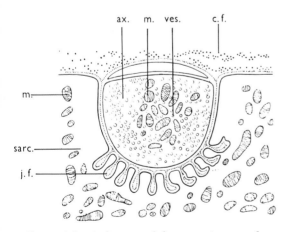

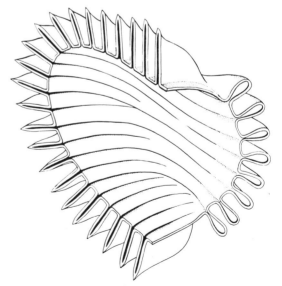

Figure 2.5. A drawing of the synaptic gutter from a neuromuscular junction of the lizard *Anolis carolinensis*, seen in cross section. *ax.*, Axon; *m.*, mitochondria; *ves.*, vesicles; *sarc.*, sarcoplasm; *j.f.*, junctional fold; *c.f.*, collagen fibrils. (From Couteaux, 1958, after Robertson, 1956, by permission of Academic Press, Inc.)

Figure 2.6. Schematic three-dimensional drawing of the subsynaptic region at the extremity of a synaptic gutter, showing the arrangement of the junctional folds. (From Couteaux, 1958, by permission of Academic Press, Inc.)

gitudinally. In the latter case the folds may be as long as the gutters themselves, and the aspect of the synaptic gutter on a section perpendicular to its axis reminds one of a part of a cogwheel, where the cogs correspond to the folds seen in the cross-section.

"In the neighbourhood of the edges of each gutter, the subneural folds have, on the contrary, a constant orientation, which is perpendicular to each edge. The arrangement of folds in these areas explains why the sections cut transversely to the gutter axis have no 'cogs' in proximity to edges, except at the gutter extremity."

The main features which characterize a synapse are therefore present in these peripheral structures, but in addition, information regarding the fitting together of the pre- and postsynaptic membranes is here completely available. At some interneuronal synapses there is also evidence for the presynaptic ending's being fitted into a depression of the postsynaptic membrane, and it is conceivable that some arrangement similar to that lining the junctional gutters may be present in those situations also.

Smooth Muscle

The innervation pattern of visceral smooth muscle is extraordinarily complex, as is well known. Earlier interpretations of the innervation patterns of the autonomic nervous system are many in number and fall into three mutually opposed groups, whose viewpoints have been summarized by Hillarp (1946) as follows: (a) The connection between nerve cells and between innervation structure and effector cell is supplied by a terminal reticulum, a nervous syncytium continuously and diffusely woven into the effector cells and directly connected with the neurofibrillar apparatus of the ganglion cells. (b) The peripheral innervation structure consists of a sympathetic ground plexus, a syncytial network of Schwann cells within which perpetually anastomosing neurofibrils are found continuously connected with the effector cells by means of a periterminal reticulum. (c) The connection between the preganglionic and the postganglionic neurone takes place via pericellular nervous structures without any neurofibrillar continuity. The postganglionic nerves form no preterminal or terminal peripheral networks, but run independent of each other. They give an individual innervation to the effector cells in the form of free, or intraprotoplasmatic, nerve endings.

From his own work Hillarp concluded that the second of these interpretations was the true one for the terminations of the postganglionic fibers on effector cells, and made the following statement to that effect:

"It has been possible to demonstrate the presence of a special nervous formation, the nervous ground plexus, both in glands and in smooth musculature. This plexus is always built in fundamentally the same way: a plexus of axons running in a dense network of anastomosing strands formed by a terminal Schwann plasmodium. The plexus is directly superimposed on the effector cells and is also found to be interwoven in between them in such a way that it seems probable that every effector cell is in direct contact with some part of it. The whole construction of the ground plexus strongly indicates that it is a closed terminal formation. The opinion that it is the true peripheral innervation structure therefore seems acceptable."

Although studies with the electron microscope have helped to clarify this situation in that it is now certain that the autonomic plexus consists of Schwann cell-sheathed nerve fibers lying within the muscle coats, the nature of the terminations of the fibers with the muscle cells is still not certain (Richardson, 1958). Occasionally, a fine nerve ending was found fitted to a depression in the surface of the muscle cell. Occasionally also, a nerve fiber filled with vesicles reminiscent of those found at other synapses was seen, and Richardson comments that if the vesiculated fibers ending in indentations on muscle cells are the only true synapses, then it is most unlikely that each muscle cell receives even one such ending.

On the other hand, Caesar, Edwards, and Ruska (1957) reported that each muscle cell could be in contact with nerves at many points along its surface, and noted that at each the covering Schwann cell was incomplete so that the naked axonal membrane was in apposition to the muscle and separated from it by a space of about 200 Å. This is analogous to the situation existing at somatic neuromuscular junctions, and is suggestive that these points of contact may be true synaptic junctions. Caesar, Edwards, and Ruska (1957) and Yamamoto (1960) state that vesicles and mitochondria within the axons are seen occasionally, but imply that this is comparatively rare. However, Caesar (1959) has published photographs showing several axons with vesicles lying in the space adjacent to a single muscle fiber (Figure 2.7), from which it may perhaps be inferred that the occurrence of such a structure is more frequent than was at one time believed. If this is the case, then also the likelihood of synaptic transmission at these junctions being mediated through a mechanism resembling that at other sites where a

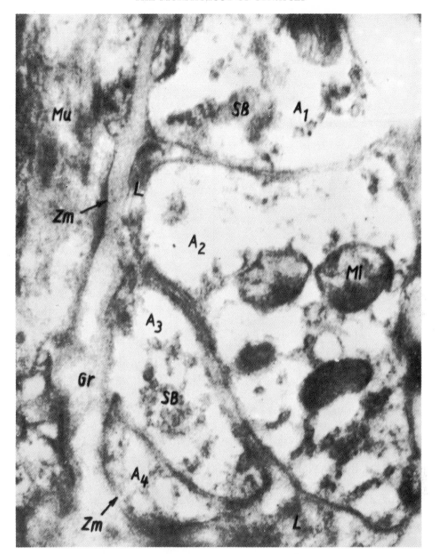

Figure 2.7. A single smooth muscle cell (*Mu*) from the bladder of a mouse, with four axons (A_1, A_2, A_3, A_4) lying adjacent to it. Two of the axons show "synaptic vesicles" (*SB*). *Mi*, Mitochondrion; *Zm*, cell membrane; *Gr*, intercellular ground substance; *L*, portions of a lemnoblast. (From Caesar, 1959, by permission of Gustav Fischer Verlag.)

generally similar type of morphology has been observed is much enhanced.

INVERTEBRATE SYNAPSES

The fine structure of many invertebrate synapses has not yet been adequately investigated. There are indications, however, that some interneuronal synapses are similar to the vertebrate ones which have been discussed in some detail. Thus, for example, de Robertis and Bennett (1955) described the presence of typical vesicles in the presynaptic ending of contacts in the nervous system of the earth-

worm. Another typical synaptic ending, of interest also in that its physiological function is known, has been described by Peterson and Pepe (1961). The sensory neurones of the stretch receptor organs of crayfish receive an inhibitory nerve supply, and the endings of these fibers make contact with all parts of the postsynaptic cell and its processes. The endings conform to the general description which we have considered above—they have an accumulation of circular vesicles 400 to 500 A in diameter; they show a concentration of mitochondria; and have an increased density of the membrane in the region where the postsynaptic cell is opposed.

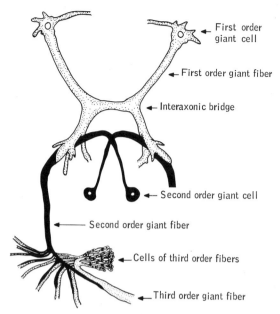

Figure 2.8. A drawing of the arrangement of the giant nerve systems in the squid *Loligo pealii.* The synapse between second and third order giant fibers has been the one particularly studied. (Adapted from Young, 1939, by permission of the Royal Society.)

There are among the invertebrates a number of synapses which by reason of their size have received the attention of physiologists. Such are found in the giant nerve system of squid, described originally by Young (1939). The arrangement, adapted from the description given by Young, is shown semischematically in Figure 2.8. Impulses which ultimately result in rapid movements of the squid are initiated in the first order cells by afferent information coming from optic and tactile, as well as from other, sources. These fibers end upon the cells as typical boutons, which are widely distributed over their surfaces. The axons emanating from the cells fuse to form an inter-axonic bridge in which the fibers from the two sides merge completely and are contained within a single membrane. Thus impulses started in one cell will be transmitted to both sides of the animal. Behind the bridge the first order axons make synaptic contact with second order giant fibers (axo-axonic synapses), whose cells lie in the pallio-visceral ganglion. The second order giant fibers in turn pass to the stellate ganglion, where again axo-axonic synapses are formed with the third order fibers. It is this final synapse which has, in particular, been studied, for the pre- and postsynaptic halves of the synapse are in this instance both so large that events occurring in

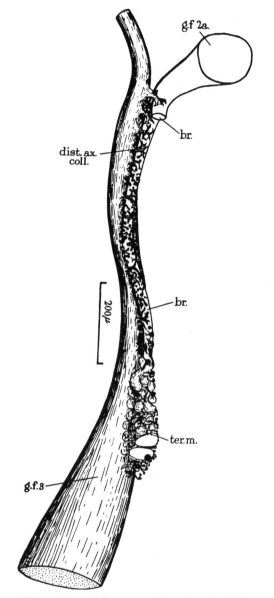

Figure 2.9. A drawing to show details of the synapse between second (*g.f.2a*) and third (*g.f.3*) order giant fibers in the squid. Small processes of the postsynaptic fiber (*dist. ax. coll.*) wrap about the second order fiber forming the synaptic junctions. (From Young, 1939, by permission of the Royal Society.)

each portion may be separately studied (see p. 58 below). A drawing of this giant synapse is given in Figure 2.9, in which the protruding processes of the postsynaptic structure towards the presynaptic fiber should be noted. The processes are densely packed with axoplasmic filaments entirely surrounded by the postsynaptic membrane, and these filaments are present in greater quantity in the post- than in the presynaptic fiber (Robertson, 1953).

The other giant synapse whose importance is such as to demand special mention here is that between the lateral giant fiber and the giant motor fiber of the third root of the abdominal ganglia of crayfish. Its main features were described by Johnson (1924), who showed that each motor fiber crossed the lateral giant axon and approached it very closely. However, there was no suggestion of a fusion between them. Later studies, both of these and of the contacts between motor and median and lateral giant fibers (Robertson, 1953, 1955; Furshpan and Potter, 1959; Hama, 1961), have revealed that as at the squid synapse the motor fiber extends processes toward the giant axon and that there is fusion of the Schwann cell membranes of the motor and median fibers to produce an axon-axon membrane (Figures 2.10 and 2.11). When account is taken of the thickness of the two bounding membranes, it is apparent that the axons approach each other very closely in these regions, being separated by a space which is not wider than 150 Å, and is probably considerably less (Furshpan and Potter, 1959; Hama, 1961). Within the motor axon processes there is an accumulation of bodies with a lamellated appearance which are present also throughout the axon, while also in the processes of both fibers are small vesicular bodies of 250 to 1000 Å in diameter, to which are frequently attached filamentous tails.

In spite of its unusual morphology, notably in that the cytoplasmic inclusion bodies are concentrated within the motor fiber (i.e., the postsynaptic structure) and are absent from, or at any rate are less numerous in, the lateral or median giant fibers, there is no doubt that this structure functions as a synapse in that impulses are passed in one direction only, from the giant fibers to the appropriate motor axons (Wiersma, 1947). It has now been found however, that the synapse between lateral and motor fibers has a fundamentally

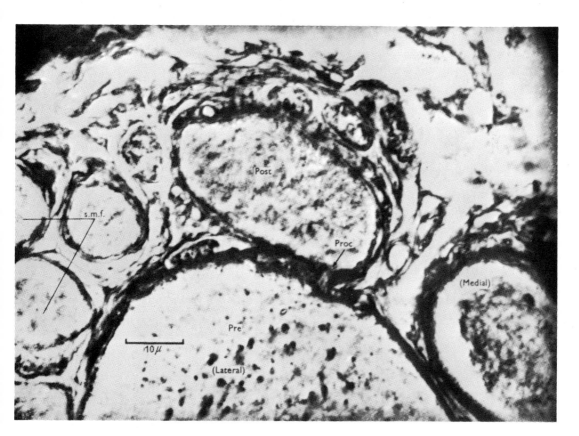

Figure 2.10. A transverse section through a crayfish nerve cord in the region of a lateral giant motor synapse. The arrow shows a synaptic process, which extends from the motor (*Post*) fiber to the lateral giant (*Pre*) fiber. The medial giant fiber (*Medial*) is seen on the right, and three smaller fibers of the motor root (*s.m.f.*) appear on the left. (From Furshpan and Potter, 1959, by permission of the Journal of Physiology.)

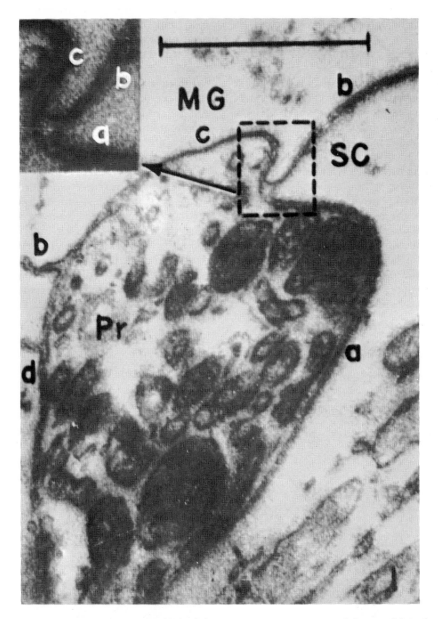

Figure 2.11. A synaptic process (*Pr*) of the postsynaptic motor axon of the crayfish is shown in the Schwann cytoplasm (*SC*). The axoplasm of the presynaptic median giant fiber (*MG*) is above. The Schwann membranes of the motor (*a*) and of the median (*b*) fibers fuse to produce an axon-axon synaptic membrane (*c*). The inset shows an enlargement of the dotted square. (From Robertson, 1955, by permission of Academic Press, Inc.)

different transmission mechanism from that operating at the synapses which we may now regard as possessing a typical morphology, i.e., ones in which the presynaptic structure is possessed of vesicles and is separated by a cleft of appreciable width from its postsynaptic partner. This unusual transmission process is considered below (p. 63). The distinction between the crayfish synapse and others is the more striking in view of the morphological similarities between it and that of the stellate ganglion of the squid. Both of these show the

close apposition of pre- and postsynaptic ending, and yet their mechanism of operation is
quite different in the two cases.

SUMMARY

The intention of this chapter has been to
show that in spite of enormously differing details of shape, many synaptic junctions from
a wide variety of sites have features which are
remarkably similar. Thus, whether the presynaptic ending is of the circumscribed type typified by the bouton terminal, or whether it is
more diffuse, as in the case of the synapses "en
passant" within the cerebellum, for example,
the submicroscopic details are the same—synaptic cleft, "vesicles" concentrated within the
cytoplasm of the presynaptic ending, and restricted glial intrusion into the region of the
synapse itself. Of those that have been discussed in some detail, only the crayfish giant
synapses exhibit significant differences from
this pattern, and it has been mentioned that
their mode of transmission is fundamentally
different from that exhibited by the others.

There are many other synapses, of course,
for which the necessary electron microscopic
data are lacking. Two of the most interesting
are: (a) those of the "spiral" synapse surrounding the axon hillock of Mauthner's cell, which
recent work has shown also to have an atypical
mechanism of action, and for which studies
to establish whether or not it conforms to the
morphological pattern of the crayfish synapses
is required and (b) the finely coiled fibers making synaptic contacts with motoneurones which
Szentágothai (1958) has described. By co-
incidence, both these synapses are inhibitory
in function. They have certain superficial
morphological resemblances, and it would be
of great interest to know whether those
similarities extend to their submicroscopic
organizations.

Chapter 3

THE CONCEPT OF CHEMICAL TRANSMISSION

The direct experimental evidence which has led to the conception that the transmission of information across synapses is mediated by the release of a specific chemical agent from the presynaptic side of the junction has been obtained entirely from studies of peripheral structures, and its applicability to the central nervous system is largely inferential. Some of the peculiar features of synaptic transmission, in contrast to conduction in the nerve fibers, were recognized early, in the days when the nature of the transmission process was quite unknown, and a large number of conflicting hypotheses sought to explain it. Sherrington (1906) described in detail some of these features of the transmission process, which may be listed as follows:

(1) The delay which occurs in reflex pathways attributable to passage of the impulse through the synaptic junctions

(2) The less close correspondence between the moment of cessation of stimulus and the moment of cessation of end-effects, i.e., after discharge

(3) A considerable resistance to the passage of a single nerve impulse, which is easily "forced" by a succession of impulses (temporal summation)

(4) The irreversibility of direction of transmission

(5) Fatiguability and susceptibility to hypoxia, drugs and anesthetics.

Various attempts were made to explain these observations in terms of electrical theory (see, e.g., Lapique, 1926).

The first suggestion that nervous effects might be mediated by the release of a specific chemical agent from the stimulated nerve was made by Elliott (1904, 1905). He had worked out in detail the similarities between sympathetic nerve stimulation and administered adrenaline, and had noted also the evident relationship between the effects of adrenaline and those of extracts of the adrenal glands which had earlier been described by Lewandowsky (1899) and confirmed by Langley (1901). In order to explain these similarities, Elliott put forward the hypothesis that the nerves actually liberated adrenaline to be the agent of their effects. The idea was not widely accepted, except by Dixon (1906, 1907), who further argued that, although no chemical entity known at that time could mimic their action, parasympathetic nerves must similarly release a chemical mediator of their effects. Dixon (1907) made an attempt to extract this parasympathetic transmitter from a dog's heart removed from the animal during vagal inhibition, and his extract was able to cause the inhibition of an isolated frog heart. Furthermore, this inhibition, like that brought about by the vagus itself, was prevented by atropine. As Dale (1934), who quotes Dixon's observations points out, it is unlikely that the extract could have contained acetylcholine, which is now known to be the substance released from postganglionic parasympathetic fibers. Nevertheless, Dixon was right in his belief in the general applicability of Elliott's proposed mechanism.

Information derived from experiments of this type was not forthcoming for many years thereafter, but in the interval the actions of a substance not then known to occur in the body were being investigated. In the course of a study of depressor agents extractable

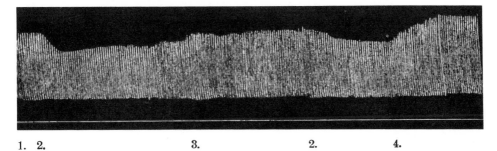

1. 2.   3.   2.   4.

Figure 3.1. The effect upon an isolated frog heart of returning to it fluid obtained during an earlier perfusion period. (*1*) During normal perfusion with Ringer solution. (*2*) Perfusion with fluid obtained during a 15 minute period of vagus stimulation. (*3*) Perfusion with fluid obtained during a 15 minute period without stimulation. (*4*) As (*2*), but with atropine added to the fluid during the stimulation period. (From Loewi, 1921, by permission of Springer Verlag.)

from the adrenal glands, Hunt (1901) conceived the idea that an ester of choline might be the active ingredient, and in 1906 Hunt and Taveau reported that the acetate ester had 1000 times the depressor action of choline itself. In 1914 Dale concluded that the brevity of the intense active phase of injected acetylcholine was probably due to its enzymatic destruction in the blood, and he commented upon the fidelity with which this substance reproduced the actions of parasympathetic stimulation just as adrenaline did those of stimulation of the sympathetic division. Dale also noted and differentiated the "muscarinic" and "nicotinic" actions of acetylcholine; the former were abolished by atropine but the latter actions, observable in autonomic ganglia, were present even after atropine administration.

The stage was thus set for the experiments of Loewi (1921), in which for the first time the release of a substance as a result of nerve stimulation which was able to exert its effects at a distance was demonstrated. Loewi showed that the perfusion fluid obtained from the isolated hearts of frogs or toads during stimulation of the vagus brought about inhibition of the heart when the fluid was returned to it, whereas fluid obtained during a period without stimulation did not have this property (Figure 3.1.). The "humoral" inhibition was prevented if atropine was added to the fluid. Loewi further observed that during perfusion of the heart from an atropinized animal, when vagal stimulation gives rise to an increase in the amplitude of the beat, the fluid imitated this effect also when returned to the heart. He concluded that "the experiments show that under the influence of the nerves inhibiting and accelerating the heart, substances having effects similar to stimulation of the respective nerves become demonstrable in the solution perfusing the heart. Under the influence of the nerve stimulation these substances therefore are either formed or liberated or they were previously formed and the cells have only now become permeable to them."[*] In the 12 years which followed this description, several other demonstrations of the liberation of an agent during nerve stimulation, which mimicked the effects of the stimulation, were reported in mammals.

The very high level of potency of the substance released in his perfusions was recognized by Loewi, who remarked on the likelihood of only a small fraction of any liberated material reaching the fluid and of its considerable dilution there. In 1922 Loewi compared the effects of his "Vagusstoff" with acetylcholine. He demonstrated the presence of choline in his perfusion fluids but, observing that its action was much weaker than that of acetylcholine, concluded that it could not be the inhibitory material. A series of papers in the next few years lent further confirmation to the conclusion that the Vagusstoff and acetylcholine were identical, although, for a reason to be mentioned shortly, the suggestion was never stated explicitly. Witanowski (1925) described some of the chemical properties of Vagusstoff. Loewi and Navratil (1926a) compared the destruction of Vagusstoff and of acetylcholine, and later (1926b) showed that the alkaloid eserine potentiated the effects of both agents. Finally, Engelhart and Loewi

[*]"Die Versuche lehren, dass unter dem Einfluss der Reizung der herzhemmenden und -fördernden Nerven Stoffe vom gleichen Wirkungscharakter, wie er der Nervreizung eignet, in der Füllflüssigkeit des Herzens nachweisbar werden. Es werden also unter dem Einfluss der Nervenreizung diese Stoffe gebildet oder abgespalten oder sie waren vorgebildet und die Zellen werden erst dafür durchgängig."

(1930) and Matthes (1930) demonstrated that the action of eserine was to prevent the enzymatic destruction of acetylcholine and that in high dilutions of the drug this action was specific.

The reluctance finally to identify Vagusstoff with acetylcholine was due to the fact that the substance had never been shown to be a constituent of the body. This impediment was overcome when Dale and Dudley (1929) succeeded in isolating and chemically characterizing it in extracts of spleen. The parallelism of action between Vagusstoff and acetylcholine upon a number of different biological test objects has been felt to render the identity of the two beyond all reasonable doubt, and the concept of postganglionic parasympathetic action being transmitted everywhere through the mediation of acetylcholine is now a commonplace of physiology.

The following list of the discoveries which led to this ultimate conclusion will be useful later when consideration is given to the pretensions of various chemical entities as transmitter substances in the central nervous system:

(1) Acetylcholine was identified as a natural product and was found later in the vagus and in other parasympathetic nerves.

(2) It is released during nerve stimulation but not during periods of rest.

(3) There exists a potent enzyme for the destruction of the released substance, and the products of hydrolysis were found to be very much less active than the parent compound.

(4) Drugs which potentiate (eserine) or prevent (atropine) the effects of nerve stimulation similarly alter the response to exogenously applied acetylcholine in a number of different test situations. The concurrence of evidence in these four categories has rendered the identification almost certain for this particular situation; nevertheless, it must be emphasized that acetylcholine has never been identified chemically in the perfusion fluid from an isolated frog heart, and the remote possibility that the transmitter is some other substance having identical physiological properties and yet differing chemically cannot be absolutely excluded. Thus, for example, the presence of a number of other esters of choline in various tissues has recently been demonstrated, and some are at least as active biologically as is acetylcholine (for references see Florey, 1961).

The concept of the liberation of a chemical substance as the immediate cause of postsynaptic change provides a ready means of explanation of two of the points noted by Sherrington. The delay during passage of an impulse through a synapse would be expected if the mechanism involved the release of a substance from the presynaptic ending, its diffusion across the synaptic cleft, and its reaction with the elements of the subsynaptic membrane leading to appropriate changes in the permeability characteristics of the latter. It would further be expected, and abundant evidence has confirmed, that synapses provide points of attack for various pharmacological agents and that they are more susceptible to fatigue than are other segments of a reflex arc. The interaction of the transmitter with the postsynaptic membrane in particular would be a likely point at which interference with the transmission process would be expected, since the chemical combination of the two is probable; and therefore other substances related structurally to the transmitter might be expected to react with the membrane but not to give rise to its normal response. Other compounds, again, might be found which would react and cause activation of the synapse, but which would be insensitive to attack by the destroying enzyme, and would thus provide prolonged action. Much fruitful pharmacological endeavor has been directed along these lines.

The "life cycle" of a transmitter substance, of which we shall consider acetylcholine the typical representative, can be broken into three main sections: its synthesis and storage; its mobilization, release and reaction with the postsynaptic structure; and its inactivation.

The synthesis of acetylcholine by brain tissue was demonstrated in 1936 by Quastel, Tennenbaum, and Wheatley, and in 1943 the enzyme responsible was given the name "choline acetylase" by Nachmansohn and Machado. Synthesis has been shown to occur probably in the mitochondria (Hebb and Smallman, 1956) and not only in the cell body but throughout the length of the axon and dendrites. It would be inappropriate here to dwell in detail upon the biochemical aspects of this process, but the prevalent notion is that choline acetylase is manufactured within the soma and thence is transferred to the endings by flow of the axoplasm (Hebb and Waites, 1956). The synthesis of the transmitter itself requires the application of metabolic energy to the system, and the various cofactors required for the production of acetylcholine by cell-free enzyme preparations have now been worked out in detail.

It was realized early that most of the acetylcholine extractable from central nervous tissue does not exist there in a "free" form, but is in some manner bound to the tissue such that it is inert physiologically and at the same time protected from destruction by cholinesterase (Mann, Tennenbaum, and Quastel, 1939). In a homogenate of brain tissue this "bound" acetylcholine could be released by a variety of chemical manipulations, and there is evidence that during the process of production of acetylcholine the bound form is synthesized first. Thus, it is evident that the process of chemical transmission involves as a first step the release of the transmitter substance from its inactive form within the presynaptic endings, whence it can diffuse across the synaptic cleft to affect the postsynaptic structure. It is therefore logical that the store of material present at any time within the tissue should be physiologically inactive, and it may perhaps be presumed that the traces of free acetylcholine found in brain after excision are due to neuronal excitation resulting from the manipulations and trauma to which the tissue has been subjected.

There is now evidence, which will be considered in detail in Chapter 5, that the release of acetylcholine at the neuromuscular junctions of vertebrates occurs in a quantal fashion, i.e., that there exists within the presynaptic ending a preformed unit of the transmitter, multiples of which are released upon the arrival of an electrical signal at the ending. A characteristic feature of synapses, as we have seen, is the accumulation of "vesicles" within the presynaptic terminal which appear to be almost all of uniform size, and many authors now accept the hypothesis that the vesicles represent the unitary stores of "bound" acetylcholine. The quantum of action therefore is held to represent the breakdown of one vesicle and the release therefrom of its contained transmitter.

Direct experimental evidence for the relationship between acetylcholine and the synaptic vesicles is not overwhelming, and there are certain difficulties in its way. Whittaker (1959) and others have prepared ultracentrifugal fractions of brain, and have demonstrated that one, apparently containing pinched-off synaptic boutons filled with vesicles, possesses a remarkably higher concentration of acetylcholine than do others. Further, cholinergic nerve fibers contain extractable acetylcholine, and vesicles have been detected at least in the nodal areas of these nerves (Robertson, 1957). How the acetylcholine,

synthesized by the mitochondria, is caused to be enclosed within the vesicles is not clear, unless these latter originate from the endoplasmic reticulum (Palade, 1956), which in turn is formed by the mitochondria (Bernhard and Rouiller, 1956). Alternatively, Birks, Huxley, and Katz (1960) have found that within nerve terminals there are aggregates of these vesicles contained by a double membrane resembling that surrounding mitochondria, and the possibility therefore exists that this is an intermediate stage in which a mitochondrion is itself transformed into vesicles, these being liberated into the cytoplasm following rupture of the membrane holding them together.

The greatest doubt cast upon this hypothesis stems from the uncertainty of the morphological identification, to which reference was made above (see p. 4). If the "vesicles" are in fact part of a continuous structure, then they cannot subserve the function suggested for them here. Furthermore, the presence of vesicles in both the pre- and postsynaptic elements of the crayfish giant synapses has been described, and there is excellent evidence that this junction is not mediated by a chemical transmission process (see p. 66). Evidently, then, the presence of vesicles is not a characteristic feature of chemically mediated synapses.

In spite of these uncertainties, however, the fact that the transmission process at many synapses is quantal in nature leads one to believe that some morphologically identifiable unit must be involved, and the vesicles are the only structures which have been described. In this connection it is to be noted that evidence exists indicating that acetylcholine present in the cytoplasm of an ending is not available for release in response to an action potential. Because of the widespread acceptance of the hypothesis, some of the conclusions which can be drawn therefrom will be discussed in some detail; but again it must be emphasized that the anatomical basis of the concept is very insecure. It is probable, however, that many of the matters to be considered here would be equally applicable to some other morphological arrangement.

The mechanism by which the quanta of acetylcholine are discharged into the synaptic cleft in response to an impulse arriving in the ending is not clear. One must picture an adhesion of the vesicle to the bounding membrane and the discharge of its contents through that membrane, possibly by means of pores which have appeared in its surface. There would seem to be two facets to the whole process which may be distinguished: (a) factors influencing the approach of the vesicles to the membrane and its combination therewith and (b) the rupture of the vesicle itself.

It is conceivable that the vesicle is a charged particle, and although the potential gradients generated by an action potential cannot be large enough to cause an appreciable movement of such a massive body, there could be local changes in the repulsive or attractive forces between membrane and vesicle, such that combination between the two becomes facilitated. The denser packing of vesicles close to the membrane region which is seen in electron photomicrographs should be remembered in this regard. An attraction between a charged vesicle and the membrane might also occur because of the alterations in the ionic composition of the axoplasm close to the membrane which occur during depolarization of an excitable cell. The size of the presynaptic impulse can in some cases be demonstrated directly to have an action upon the output of transmitter from the endings. Thus Hagiwara and Tasaki (1958) were able to show that a reduction by one-fifth in the amplitude of an incoming action potential almost completely prevented the transmission

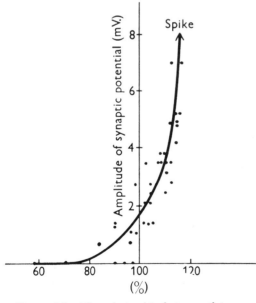

Figure 3.2. The relationship between the presynaptic action potential (abscissa) and the amplitude of the postsynaptic potential at the squid giant synapse. The size of the presynaptic spike was altered by an applied polarization of the ending. (From Hagiwara and Tasaki, 1958, by permission of the Journal of Physiology.)

process, due to the failure of release of the transmitter (Figure 3.2). Liley (1956b) had evidence for the same effect at mammalian neuromuscular junctions.

Such ionic alterations could well lead to the breakdown of the vesicles themselves. The ionic species involved is certainly not potassium, for the release of acetylcholine following increases in extracellular potassium are secondary to the depolarization which this procedure induces. Hutter and Kostial (1955) claimed that the release of acetylcholine was unaffected by the complete removal of extracellular sodium, but this has been questioned by Quastel and Birks (1962), who have reported that both synthesis and release of the transmitter are depressed. Sodium ions therefore may contribute to the mobilization. The presence of extracellular calcium is also essential for the liberation of acetylcholine (Harvey and MacIntosh, 1940), and changes in its concentration affect the number of quanta contributing to each synaptic event (del Castillo and Katz, 1954). Magnesium, which in contrast to calcium is present in appreciable concentration intracellularly, depresses acetylcholine release when present in the environmental fluid (del Castillo and Engbaek, 1954). The suggestion has been made, therefore, that the depolarization of the terminal caused by the arrival of an action potential results in the influx of calcium, and that this facilitates the breakdown of the vesicles and the liberation of acetylcholine. Intracellular calcium is extruded only slowly (Hodgkin and Keynes, 1957), and it is possible that the enhanced acetylcholine release which follows repetitive activation of the endings may be related to this fact. Similar effects of calcium and magnesium upon the liberation of single quanta of acetylcholine at neuromuscular junctions have been demonstrated by Hubbard (1961). The importance of calcium for the release of catecholamines from the adrenal medulla in response to acetylcholine has been demonstrated (Douglas and Rubin, 1961a), and it is interesting that acetylcholine has been shown greatly to increase the uptake of calcium by the gland (Douglas and Rubin, 1961b).

Many neurones characteristically discharge action potentials at high frequencies (the synapses between afferent fibers and the cells of the spinocerebellar tracts described by Holmqvist, Lundberg, and Oscarsson (1956) provide a striking example), and the question of the mobilization of transmitter and the maintenance of an adequate supply within the terminals is therefore of fundamental importance. Eccles (1961b) has calculated that at typical boutons upon motoneurones the arrival of an impulse would result in the breakdown of two or three vesicles, and that each ending would have a reserve for about 10,000 impulses preformed within it. Similar calculations for other synapses yield figures of about the same order. Prolonged repetitive synaptic activation, especially at high frequencies, therefore raises the question not only of the manner in which vesicles are brought into position to prepare for discharge, but also regarding their rapid reconstitution. At motoneuronal synapses the maximum liberation of transmitter per unit of time occurs at frequencies above 300/sec. (Curtis and Eccles, 1960).

It is worth noting that de Robertis (1958) has claimed that prolonged intense stimulation results in depletion of vesicles from nerve endings which, if the correlation between them and quanta of transmitter is true, might be expected. However this finding has not been confirmed by Birks, Huxley, and Katz (1960) at neuromuscular junctions, and one would have to postulate an extremely rapid rate of resynthesis in the latter situation to account for the discrepancy. De Robertis also reported that at a lower frequency of stimulation the number of vesicles observed in an ending was actually increased, which suggested that a mechanism for their synthesis had been triggered into activity by the applied stimuli. It is possible that another aspect of the same mechanism has been described by Brown, Davies, and Ferry (1961), who showed that the output of adrenergic transmitter from a spleen which had been deprived for some hours of its normal innervation was low, but could be greatly increased by a conditioning train of stimuli. It is obvious that we have as yet barely begun to understand these problems, yet they are clearly of fundamental significance to the whole operation of synaptic junctions.

The next step to be considered in the process of synaptic transmission is the reaction of the liberated agent with the membrane of the postsynaptic cell. Here again our knowledge is relatively scanty. It is reasonable to assume that some form of electrostatic or even of chemical combination occurs between the two, and therefore that there are "receptor patches" upon the subsynaptic membrane which are capable of such reactions. It is likely that all transmitters are ions—this is true for acetyl-

choline and for noradrenaline, and there is some evidence that the agent liberated at monosynaptic excitatory junctions upon motoneurones is an anion (see Eccles, 1961b), and that the inhibitory transmitter may be a cation (McLennan, 1960a). The concept of the reaction of the transmitter with receptor areas of the membrane is now widely accepted, and an understanding of the mode of action of many pharmacological agents which block synaptic transmission can be explained in terms of competition of the drug with the transmitter for the receptor sites. The chemical similarity of many such agents to the transmitter whose action they antagonize is evidence eloquent enough.

The changes evoked in the subsynaptic membrane by the operation of a transmitter substance are always in the direction of increasing its resting permeability to ions and, as will be considered in Chapter 4, this increased penetration may be for all small ions in some cases while in others it is restricted to those below a certain rather critical diameter. There is a widespread tendency at the present time to ascribe the increased conductance of the activated membrane to the appearance of pores in its surface, and at some synapses these are considered to be of too small a bore to permit the movement of ions above the critical size. The function of the transmitter is thus regarded as in some manner removing a "trap door" from the pore, which falls back into place when the active phase of transmitter action is over.

This picture is undoubtedly an oversimplification which it can only be hoped is not too misleading. Even non-living membranes can function as ionic sieves, and in biological systems there can be no question but that, for example, the pore size can increase suddenly during depolarization of an axon, such that sodium ions are able much more freely to penetrate into the axoplasm. What is completely inadequate is our understanding of what changes on the molecular level occur in structure of the membrane substance to permit these alterations in porosity.

It is possible that the combination of transmitter agent and subsynaptic membrane may be closely connected with the inactivation of the active material. The enzyme responsible for the hydrolysis and inactivation of acetylcholine is called cholinesterase, and the affinity of the enzyme for its substrate is enormously high. There seems little doubt that at cholinergic synapses this enzyme could effectively terminate the active phase of transmitter action. That such an arrangement may not occur at some non-cholinergic synapses is a subject which will be further discussed in Chapter 6.

There is excellent evidence that the enzyme is localized to the synaptic areas of vertebrate skeletal muscle (see Figure 5.2.) and that at these cholinergic synapses there can be comparatively little leakage of the transmitter away from the site of its primary action. It is tempting to consider that the hydrolyzing enzyme and the active receptive areas of the subsynaptic membrane may be actually identical, and there are similarities in the reactions of the enzyme and the receptors to some synthetic esters of choline which would tend to support this view. Nevertheless there is little definitive evidence either to confirm or to eliminate the concept (see, e.g., the discussion by Wilson and Nachmansohn, 1954). Perhaps one more recent piece of evidence which would tend to speak against it is the finding by Birks and Brown (1960) that in sections of neuromuscular junctions examined with the electron microscope and stained for cholinesterase, the largest concentrations of enzyme were found adjacent to, but not actually part of, the synaptic membranes. Some of the superficial parts only of the folded postsynaptic membrane also indicated the presence of the material, but the greater area of membrane which presumably included the receptor patches was free of it. Barnett (1962) has, however, found cholinesterase to be present not only associated with the postjunctional membrane, but also on the presynaptic side, within the synaptic cleft itself, and on the synaptic vesicles. Although there can be some doubt about the reliability of the histochemical method at very high magnifications, it is clear that a complete understanding of the precise role of the enzyme in the transmission process has not been attained.

The fact that some authors have found evidence for cholinesterase localization only away from the primary reactive areas would seem to imply a dissolution of the transmitter from the subsynaptic membrane, and its diffusion away through the cleft as a necessary prelude to its inactivation. Ogston (1955) has shown that diffusion from a space of simple geometry could adequately account for the decay of transmitter action without the necessity of invoking enzymatic destruction of the agent; and Eccles and Jaeger (1958) extended the same considerations to synapses of more

complex shape. The arguments are complicated both by the uncertain and difficult geometries exhibited by many synapses and by the fact that liberation of the transmitter into the cleft is not uniform, but occurs in discrete quanta, and therefore there will be some zones of the subsynaptic membrane receiving intense activation and other zones receiving comparatively little.

It seems certain that at vertebrate neuromuscular junctions there is insufficient time available for diffusion of the liberated acetylcholine in any appreciable amount into the depths of the infoldings lining the synaptic gutters, and it is possible that this is to be correlated with the fact that cholinesterase is said by some to be absent from those deep regions. It would further seem reasonable to consider that the process of inactivation of the acetylcholine, which must ultimately involve its hydrolysis by cholinesterase, may be in large part preceded by diffusion of the material out of the cleft, and that its main

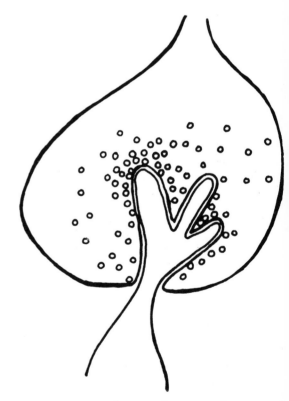

Figure 3.3. A drawing of a synapse between rod receptor and postsynaptic cell in the retina of the rabbit. Note the invagination of the postsynaptic element into the presynaptic terminal. (From Eccles and Jaeger, 1958, after de Robertis and Franchi, 1956, by permission of the Royal Society.)

points of destruction lie at the borders of the gutter where the concentration of cholinesterase has been observed to be highest. In this concept the primary act in inactivation and termination of transmitter effect would be physical diffusion, and chemical destruction of the substance would be a later step.

There are two other matters which bear upon this question. Eccles and Jaeger (1958) have remarked upon the unusual synapses found in the retina (Figure 3.3) in which the postsynaptic structure is invaginated into the presynaptic ending. From the cleft between these, diffusion may be presumed to be considerably impeded, and there is evidence that a prolonged transmitter action is involved at these synapses. The same would seem to be true for the cholinergic synapses between motor axon collaterals and the Renshaw cells of the spinal cord. These cells respond to a single presynaptic impulse by a prolonged burst of firing, which implies that there is a long phase of transmitter action. This prolonged period (up to 50 msec.) of synaptic excitation has recently been directly observed (Eccles, Eccles, Iggo, and Lundberg, 1961). The synapses themselves appear to be typical boutons (see p. 5), and one is forced therefore to the conclusion that some other and unidentified type of "synaptic barrier" is present which prevents the rapid breakdown at least of a portion of the acetylcholine released. (For a further discussion of synaptic barriers, see p. 80).

The same conclusion regarding the fundamental importance of diffusion to transmitter inactivation can be reached from another point of view. The catecholamines, which are liberated at adrenergic synapses, are inactivated in the body by the enzymes monoamine oxidase and O-methyl transferase. Both of these, however, are comparatively slow in operation, and whereas cholinesterase could inactivate its substrate sufficiently rapidly to account for synaptic events, it seems unlikely that this could occur at adrenergic sites. The problem is obviated, however, if diffusion is allowed the primary role, with the enzymatic processes taking place only later. Such mechanisms could be invoked to explain many of the differences in the lengths of time over which any given transmitter agent is active, i.e., both the chemical nature of the substance and the affinity between it and its destroying enzyme on the one hand and the complexity of the diffusional path between the sites of action and of destruction of the transmitter

will contribute to the over-all effect, and such combined effects may be expected to show very great ranges of duration. Such are, in fact, observed (see Table IV).

In conclusion, the considerations made in this chapter may be summarized in the form of a list of criteria which must be satisfied by any substance which is thought to be acting as a transmitter of synaptic action. This list will be referred to again, when in Chapter 6 the evidence for certain substances being synaptic transmitters in the central nervous system will be considered.

(1) The substance must occur in those neurones, including their processes, whose actions it transmits at the synapses it forms with ensuing neurones or target organs.

(2) The neurone must possess an enzymatic mechanism for the synthesis of the substance.

(3) There must be an enzyme system present for the inactivation of the substance, which may or may not be localized to the postsynaptic membrane.

(4) Application of the substance to the postsynaptic structure should mimic the action of stimulation of the neurone.

(5) During stimulation the substance should be detectable in extracellular fluid collected from the region of the activated synapses.

(6) Pharmacological agents which interfere with the operation of the neurone should similarly affect the action of the substance artificially applied. Such actions may be divided into three groups: (a) those which interfere with the intracellular synthesis of the substance and which should therefore lead to failure of action of the neurone; (b) those which interfere with the release or the reaction of the substance with the postsynaptic membrane and thereby block its effect; and (c) those which block the destroying enzyme and which should lead to a prolongation of the effect of the substance and of stimulation of the neurone.

This list of criteria may be useful in the assessment of the likelihood of any substance being active as a transmitter of synaptic activity. However, as has been pointed out by Florey (1960a), the satisfaction of any one of these is quite insufficient to establish a transmitter function for a compound, and some may be met by a substance which does not act as a transmitter at all. This is evident for points 1, 2 and 3, while 5 could be satisfied by any material which might be liberated from the activated endings together with the true transmitter. Finally, substances are known which can either enhance or depress neuronal function independently of synaptic effects, and these may not be easy to differentiate from the blocking or potentiation of transmitter action. It can only be said that if most or all of the listed points are met, the likelihood that a given substance acts as a transmitter is rendered highly probable.

Chapter 4

SYNAPTIC EVENTS AT MOTONEURONES

There are two principal reasons why the motoneurones of vertebrates, and especially of the cat's spinal cord, have been selected for intensive study of synaptic mechanisms. One is that the connections of the motoneurone with other cells of the central nervous system, while by no means entirely elucidated, are by comparison well understood, and the various reflex arcs in which it is involved can be isolated and studied uncomplicated by influences difficult to control or even unrecognized. The second is its size: again by comparison the motoneurone is a large cell, and inasmuch as the greatest part of our knowledge of synaptic events has come from studies of electrical changes produced across the neuronal membrane, which in turn has required the introduction of a microelectrode into the cell, the larger size has allowed records to be obtained from relatively undamaged structures and

over appreciable periods of time. The dimensions of a typical mammalian motoneurone are indicated in Figure 4.1. It has a soma of about 70 μ across, from which a number of long dendrites (up to 1 mm) radiate before they break up into fine terminal branches. The dendrites have a diameter of 5 to 6 μ. The axon emerges from the conical axon hillock of the soma, and is unmyelinated for 50 to 100 μ, after which it acquires a myelin sheath. Axon hillock and unmyelinated axon are together known as the initial segment. Eccles (1957) has calculated the volume and surface area of a typical motoneurone, including the dendrites up to 300 μ from the soma, to be 2.5 $\times$ 10^{-7} cm^3 and 5 $\times$ 10^{-4} cm^2 respectively; these cells thus are 10 times larger than the largest pyramidal tract neurones of the cerebral cortex. The arrangement of synaptic boutons over much of the somatic and proximal dendritic membranes has been described in detail earlier.

It will be profitable at this point to summarize the spinal reflex arcs in which the motoneurone is involved and in which it plays a role as the final integrating center for influences from the various sources which impinge upon it. It must not be forgotten that all the types of action set forth in Table I are constantly exerting effects upon each motoneurone, and therefore that all have synaptic representation there. Further, it must be remembered that this list does not exhaust the connections received by the motoneurone, in that it does not include influences from higher centers of the central nervous system which may lead also to excitation or to inhibition of motoneuronal activity. There is, however, no

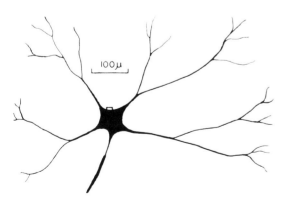

Figure 4.1. A drawing of a motoneurone of the mammalian spinal cord to illustrate the general relationships of dendrites and axon to the soma. (From Eccles, 1957, by permission of Johns Hopkins Press.)

TABLE I. REFLEX ACTIONS OF MAMMALIAN SPINAL MOTONEURONES *

Ending	Fiber	Pathway	Effect Upon Motoneurone
Annulospiral	Homonymous Ia	Direct	Monosynaptic excitation
Annulospiral	Heteronymous synergistic Ia	Direct	Excitation
Annulospiral	Heteronymous antagonistic Ia	Via Ia interneurones of intermediate nucleus	"Direct" inhibition
Golgi tendon	Homonymous Ib	Via Ib interneurones	Inhibition
Golgi tendon	Heteronymous antagonistic Ib	Via Ib interneurones	Excitation
Flower-spray	II	Via interneurones	Inhibition**
Free	III	Via Ia interneurones	Inhibition**
Free	Cutaneous	Via Ia interneurones	Inhibition**
—	Motor axon collaterals	Renshaw cells	Inhibition

* The effects listed are for an extensor motoneurone subjected to ipsilateral afferent stimulation. For a flexor neurone, the actions marked **
would be reversed. Contralateral Ia and Ib stimulation on an extensor neurone would yield, respectively, inhibition and excitation.
Contralateral II, III, or cutaneous impulses would excite an extensor neurone (crossed extensor and Phillipson's reflexes).

reason to believe that synaptic events initiated in spinal neurones from supraspinal sources differ from those which we will consider in detail in this chapter.

It is usual and convenient to divide the various afferent fibers entering the cord into groups on the basis of their diameter (Lloyd, 1943). The groups are: group I, fibers of largest diameter (11 to 21 μ), in turn subdivided into Ia, containing those fibers emanating from the primary (annulo-spiral or nuclear bag) endings of the muscle spindles, and Ib, fibers from the Golgi tendon organs; group II (6 to 12 μ), fibers emanating also from the muscle spindles, presumably from the secondary (flower-spray or myotube) endings; and group III (1 to 6 μ), fibers from free nerve endings. Since there is a correlation between fiber diameter and threshold for excitation, it is possible to select the afferent fibers included in a given reflex arc by varying the intensity of the applied stimulation. Thus, even within group I there is a sufficient difference in size so that Ia may be excited with little contamination from Ib influence (Bradley and Eccles, 1953). If the threshold for excitation of Ia fibers is taken as 1.0, that for Ib is about 1.6; group II, 2.1; and group III, 4.0 (Coombs, Curtis, and Landgren, 1956).

THE RESTING POTENTIAL

Motoneurones, like all excitable tissue cells, exhibit at rest a steady potential difference between the cytoplasm and the external environment. Earlier methods of estimating the size of this potential have been completely supplanted by the introduction of microelectrode techniques, in which a suitably small electrode is inserted through the cell membrane and the potential difference between this lead and an indifferent electrode in contact with the extracellular fluid is measured after direct-coupled amplification and display on a suitable recording device.

Microelectrodes for intracellular recording of potential changes were first used by Ling and Gerard (1949), who introduced into muscle cells fine glass capillaries filled with a conducting solution (usually 2 to 3 M KCl) and connected to an amplifier by means of a chlorided silver wire. Since then, other microelectrodes, including ones of very fine metal or of metal-filled glass capillaries, etc., have been devised for various purposes. However,

for recording from neurones, capillaries filled with a salt solution have provided the only really useful electrodes, since these can be more dependably made with the necessarily small dimensions. The tip diameter of an electrode should be not more than 0.2 μ, and if filled with 3M KCl it will have a resistance of about 30 M Ω.

The entry of the electrode into a motoneurone is signaled by the appearance of a potential which averages –70 mV, with a range of –60 to –80 (Brock, Coombs, and Eccles, 1952; Woodbury and Patton, 1952; Coombs, Eccles, and Fatt, 1955a; Frank and Fuortes, 1955). Low values or potentials that decline appreciably with time are presumably indicative of damage to the cell. In the absence of such signs and without stimulation, the resting potential remains steady, and there is evidence that the potential is the same throughout the whole neuronal cytoplasm, including that of the dendrites and axon (see, e.g., Eyzaguirre and Kuffler, 1955a).

As do many other tissues, brain shows upon analysis a higher content of potassium than of sodium ions, which is due to the high concentration of K within the cells. There are, however, considerable difficulties in the way of arriving at reliable values for the intracellular concentration of these ionic species, and at present no way of distinguishing between neurones and other cells of the central nervous system. Table II collects some data from various authors which summarize the available information.

The calculated values for the intracellular ionic concentrations in Table II do not agree in some cases with those than can be estimated from electrophysiological data. There is evidence (Eccles, 1957) that the equilibrium potential for the hyperpolarization following an action potential in a motoneurone is close to that for potassium ions, and this potential has been estimated as –88.5 mV on the average (Coombs, Eccles, and Fatt, 1955b). Substitution of this value in the Nernst equation gives a figure of 28 $\times$ K_o for the intracellular potassium concentration (K_i). Coombs, Eccles, and Fatt state that "the external ionic concentrations may be assumed to be those of an ultrafiltrate of cat's plasma," and although it is not entirely certain that this assumption can be justified, it has been accepted here. K_i would then be 146 mM/1, which is not far from the value in Table II estimated from analytical data. By analogy with the situation existing in invertebrate

TABLE II. APPROXIMATE IONIC CONCENTRATIONS AND EQUILIBRIUM POTENTIALS
IN MAMMALIAN CENTRAL NERVOUS SYSTEM

	Plasma Ultrafiltrate mM/l. Conway (1947), Elliott and Jasper (1949), Davson (1955)	Whole Brain mM/kg. Eichelberger and Richter (1944), Pappius and Elliott (1956), Cummins and McIlwain (1961)	Intracellular Concentration* mM/l.	Equilibrium Potential † mV
Na	130	50	46	+27.5
K	5.2	108	134.5	-86.5
Cl	110	33	27.5	-36.5

* Calculated assuming an extracellular (inulin) space of 10% (McLennan, 1957a) and a dry weight of 20% (Pappius and Elliott, 1956; Cummins and McIlwain, 1961) for brain tissue.

† Calculated by the Nernst equation $E = RT/F \ln C_o/C_i$ or $E = RT/F \ln A_i/A_o$, where C and A refer to cation and anion concentrations, and the subscripts o and i to extracellular and intracellular compartments respectively.

giant nerve fibers, where axoplasm and surroundings can be separately analyzed, Na_i would be expected to be about $1/10 \times Na_o$, i.e., 13 mM/1, and substitution of this value would give an equilibrium potential for sodium ions (E_{Na}) of +60 mV. Similarly, Cl_i calculated in Table II appears high: the ratio $\dfrac{Cl_o}{Cl_i}$ for squid axons is 14 (Keynes and Lewis, 1951), and using this ratio would yield Cl_i for mammalian neurones as 8 mM/1, which in turn would give E_{Cl} as –70 mV.

These discrepancies may be due partially to the fact that analyses of whole brain include the contents of glial cells as well as those of neurones, and a suggestion has been made that the former may have a higher sodium and lower potassium content than do the latter. If this were so, then the estimates for the internal ionic compositions of neurones derived from analytical and electrical sources might become reconciled. Since analytical values, especially for Na and Cl, may be in large error from uncertainties in the allowance for the extracellular space, and since there may be inhomogeneities between the various types of cells, the data derived from electrophysiological measurements have been preferred in the ensuing discussions.

In any event, it is evident that in neurones, as in other nervous structures, the calculated equilibrium potential for sodium ions is very far from the observed level of the resting potential. At a resting potential of –70 mV the electrochemical potential for these ions is at least 100 mV, so that the inward diffusional flux must be many times greater than the outward movement due to passive physical forces. Again as in other tissues (Hodgkin and Keynes, 1955), an active transport mechanism for these ions must be postulated, the magnitude of whose effect must be sufficient almost to balance the inward flux from passive forces. An oppositely directed pump must also exist in order to maintain the high level of K_i. At a resting potential of –70 mV substitution in the Nernst equation would indicate that $14 \times K_o$ (= 73 mM/1) of K is held by the potential difference, while the remainder must be actively transported against an electrochemical gradient of 15 to 20 mV. In this instance therefore the pump has to account only for about one-half of the total internal concentration of the cation.

There is no evidence that in neurones an active transport mechanism for the movement of chloride exists, i.e., this species is in electro-chemical equilibrium in the resting state. It would appear therefore that the calculated value of 8 mM/1 for Cl_i is probably approximately correct, and that the distribution of the ion is controlled by and does not control the level of the resting potential. The identity of the remaining anionic constituents of neurones is not certainly known. There are present in the brain relatively high concentrations of glutamate, aspartate, and gamma-aminobutyrate; if the total amino nitrogen of brain is assumed to be intracellular, the concentration of amino acids would be about 40 mM/1 (Ansell and Richter, 1954). Therefore, even if this assumption were true, the identity of a considerable proportion of the negatively charged constituents of the cells remains to be ascertained.

The use of micro recording methods to measure accurately events occurring across a cellular membrane was made vastly more productive by Coombs, Eccles, and Fatt (1955a), who introduced the use of double-barreled electrodes (Figure 4.2). By means of this device, current can be applied between one barrel and an external indifferent point, while any potential change can simultaneously be recorded through the second barrel. Similar results to those about to be described have been obtained by others who have used a single microelectrode and a bridge technique

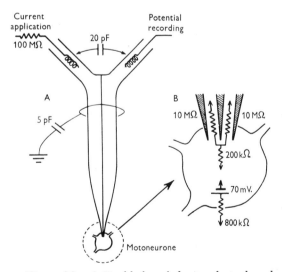

Figure 4.2. A, Double-barreled microelectrode and its immediate connections. Typical values are given of the significant electrical characteristics. In B, an enlarged view of the tip of the electrode within a motoneurone is shown. Values of the resting potential and membrane resistance are given. (From Coombs, Eccles, and Fatt, 1955a, by permission of the Journal of Physiology.)

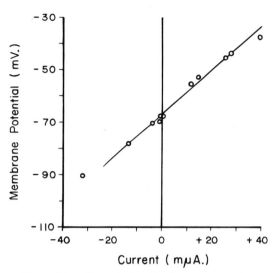

Figure 4.3. The relationship between membrane potential recorded through one barrel of a double electrode and the current applied through the other. The resting potential of the cell (i.e., at 0 current) was –67 mV, and the slope of the line gives a measure of the membrane resistance. (From Coombs, Eccles, and Fatt, 1955a, by permission of the Journal of Physiology.)

to permit the measurement of potential change under conditions of an applied current (e.g., Araki and Otani, 1955). Figure 4.3 shows a graph of the results obtained with a typical motoneurone, in which both hyperpolarizing and depolarizing currents were applied to shift the resting potential from its initial level of –67 mV. The slope of the line gives a measure of the membrane resistance, which in this instance was 0.75 M Ω. Coombs, Eccles, and Fatt (1955a) reported values ranging from 0.4 to 1.3 M Ω, and Coombs, Curtis, and Eccles (1959) reported values ranging from 0.6 to 2.5 M Ω. Assuming a total dynamic resistance of 1.2 M Ω and an area of 5 $\times$ 10^{-4} cm^2, the average specific membrane resistance of motoneurones is thus 600 Ω–cm^2.

If a constant current is suddenly applied across a motoneuronal membrane, the voltage is not developed across it equally suddenly. There is thus a capacitative component to the membrane in addition to the resistive one discussed above, and time is required for the change on the capacitor to change before a voltage is fully developed across the resistor. As the voltage develops exponentially, the "time constant" of the process is defined as that time required for it to reach $(1 - 1/e)$ of its full value. This time constant of a motoneuronal membrane can also be estimated with the aid of a double-barreled microelectrode, although an uncertain correction must be applied for changes in the electrical properties of the electrode itself due to the passage of the current (Coombs, Curtis, and Eccles, 1959). If the time constant (τ) of the system is measured in seconds and the membrane resistance (R) in ohms, the value of the membrane capacitance (C) in farads can be calculated from the expression τ = R.C. Inserting the average values obtained gives C equal to 3 $\times$ 10^{-9} F, which with a surface area of 5 $\times$ 10^{-4} cm^2 yields a specific capacitance of 6 μF/cm^2.

One final characteristic of the resting motoneurone which must be considered is the length constant, λ. In a cable, if a voltage is applied at one end, the attenuation of the signal is a function of the distance which it travels and of the resistances of its bounding sheath and of the conducting core. In a neurone, if R_m is the membrane resistance and R_c that of the cytoplasm, then $\lambda = \sqrt{R_m/R_c}$. The length constant is of importance in considering the electrotonic propagation of an electrical signal resulting from synaptic action in the dendrites of a motoneurone, for such electrotonic spread is similar to that occurring in a cable, i.e., there is a decremental conduction. It is probable that the conductivity of the cytoplasm is little, if any, lower than that of the extracellular fluid (cf. Hodgkin and Keynes, 1953; Harris, 1954), and therefore R_c may be given a value of about 50 Ω –cm. R_m is known (600 Ω–cm^2) and therefore λ is approximately 350 μ. This means that a signal initiated at the emergence of a dendrite from the soma will have decayed to 1/e of its initial size after having traversed 350 μ, and conversely that signals originating far out on the dendrites of a motoneurone will have only a negligible effect upon the reactions of the cell body (see p. 38).

Table III lists these various electrical constants as they have been determined for a number of different neurones, for comparison with the motoneuronal values which have been discussed in detail here. It is evident that the values for the membrane time constant (and therefore for the capacitance) vary more extensively than do the other constants; and this will be reflected in the varying times over which the synaptic potentials, to be discussed below, are effective. However, even quantitatively the variation is less than might have been expected from the diversity of the sources of the neurones examined.

TABLE III. SOME ELECTRICAL PROPERTIES OF RESTING NEURONAL MEMBRANES

Cell	Animal	Resting Potential (mV)	Sp. Membrane Resistance (Ω –cm^2)	Sp. Membrane Capacitance (μF/cm^2)	Time Constant (msec.)	References
Motoneurones	Cat	–70	600	6	2.9	Coombs, Eccles, and Fatt (1955a); Curtis and Eccles (1959)
Motoneurones	Toad	–65	240	17	4.0	Araki and Otani (1955)
Sympathetic ganglion cells	Frog	–67	600	20	11.5	Nishi and Koketsu (1960)
Supramedullary cells	Puffer fish	–66	500	30	15	Bennett, Crain, and Grundfest (1959)
Ganglion cells	Aplysia depilans	–40	2200	23	50	Fessard and Tauc (1956)
Cardiac ganglion cells	Lobster	–60	3000	7	21	Hagiwara, Watanabe, and Saito (1959)

THE EXCITATORY POSTSYNAPTIC POTENTIAL

Early methods of recording of the electrical signs of synaptic activation, e.g., by Schaefer and Haass (1939), involved the use of extracellular leads, and these too have given way entirely to recording with intracellular microelectrodes. If a microelectrode is inserted into a motoneurone, and the group Ia fibers in its muscle nerve are liminally stimulated, a potential change is recorded as occurring across the neuronal membrane. Typically, this potential begins about 0.5 msec. after the nerve volley has entered the cord, rises to a summit in a further 1 to 1.5 msec., and thereafter decays with an approximately exponential time course which has a time constant of 3.5 to 6.1 msec. (average 4.9 msec.) (Brock, Coombs, and Eccles, 1952; Woodbury and Patton, 1952; Coombs, Eccles, and Fatt, 1955c; Frank and Fuortes, 1955; Curtis and Eccles, 1959). This potential change, which is a characteristic of the postsynaptic cell, has been named the excitatory postsynaptic potential (EPSP) (Coombs, Eccles, and Fatt, 1955c).

If the strength of the afferent volley is increased, the amplitude of the EPSP is also raised; this fact is shown in Figure 4.4, in which the upper trace in each record was obtained from the posterior root and the lower from a motoneurone of the medial gastrocnemius muscle. It is noteworthy that although

Figure 4.5 The convergence of excitatory synaptic action upon a peroneus longus motoneurone. Maximal group Ia volleys were delivered to the nerves from peroneus brevis (*PB*), extensor digitorum longus (*EDL*), and peroneus longus (*PL*) and by all three together. Summation in amplitude of the EPSP occurred without change in its time course. (From Eccles, 1961b, after Eccles, Eccles, and Lundberg, 1957, by permission of Springer Verlag.)

the amplitude of the EPSP can be increased, its time course remains unchanged. This feature is also observed when EPSP's are produced in a motoneurone receiving monosynaptic innervation from several afferent sources, as in the example of Figure 4.5. Here a peroneus longus motoneurone responded with very similar EPSP's to maximal Ia volleys in the nerves from peroneus brevis, extensor digitorum longus, and peroneus longus; and by an arithmetic sum of the three when all the nerves were excited together.

It is evident then that the production of the EPSP is based upon a very different mechanism from that giving rise to the action potential of a nerve cell or fiber, for it is a graded response whose size varies with the intensity of the applied stimulation. Its amplitude never exceeds 20 mV, for usually at a level considerably below this the motoneurone will respond by the production of an action potential (see p. 36).

The inference to be drawn from the observed graded nature of the EPSP is that it represents a summation of some unitary activity. We have seen above that the concept of the chemical mediation of synaptic transmission requires that an impulse arriving in the presynaptic terminal cause the release from it of a quantity of transmitter, and since the amplitude of the impulse traveling to the ending down the axon is fixed, i.e., is of an all-or-nothing nature, it may be supposed that under ordinary circumstances the amount of transmitter applied to the postsynaptic cell from an activated synapse is also constant. It follows therefore that the unitary action being summed to produce the EPSP is that of individual synapses, and since the time course of the EPSP is the same irrespective of its size, we may conclude that the time course of the potential change produced at each synapse is very similar. A spatial summation of

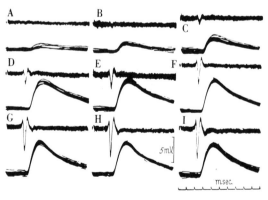

Figure 4.4. Monosynaptic EPSP's recorded in a medial gastrocnemius motoneurone of the cat in response to increasing afferent volleys, as indicated by the upper traces of each record, in the medial gastrocnemius nerve. It should be noted that although the EPSP increased in amplitude (from *A* to *F*, when the afferent volley was maximal for group Ia fibers), its time course remained unchanged. (From Eccles, 1961b, after Eccles, Eccles, and Lundberg, 1957, by permission of Springer Verlag.)

Cell	Excitatory Synapses				Inhibitory Synapses		Ref.
	Resting pot. (mV)	Time const. of decay (msec.)	Eqm. pot. (mV)	Threshold for spike (mV)	Time const. of decay (msec.)	Eqm. pot. mV	
Mammalian motoneurone	-70	5	0	10	3.5	-80	1
Frog motoneurone	-55	7.5	-	10	-	-	2
Frog sympathetic ganglia	-	12	-15	25			3
Frog neuromuscular junction	-90	5.5	-15	40			4
Mammalian neuromuscular junction	-70	2	-	15			
Crustacean neuromuscular junction	-60	20	-	-		-60	5,6
Aplysia, ganglion cells	-50	120	-	10	45	-60	7
Lobster cardiac ganglion cells	-60	20	-10	-			8
Crayfish stretch receptor neurones	-75				16	-70	9
Squid stellate ganglion	-60	1.5	0	10			10

References:
1. Curtis and Eccles (1959)
2. Machne, Fadiga, and Brookhart (1959)
3. Nishi and Koketsu (1960)
4. Fatt and Katz (1951)
5. Hoyle and Wiersma (1958 a, b)
6. Boistel and Fatt (1958)
7. Tauc (1958)
8. Hagiwara, Watanabe, and Saito (1959)
9. Kuffler and Eyzaguirre (1955)
10. Hagiwara and Tasaki (1958)

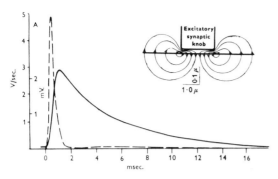

Figure 4.6. The observed EPSP (solid line) and calculated generating current (broken line) in a motoneurone with resting potential –66 mV and membrane time constant 3.6 msec. The inset shows the direction of current flow under an active excitatory ending. (From Curtis and Eccles, 1959, by permission of the Journal of Physiology.)

individual synaptic events leads to the observable EPSP.

If the time constant of the membrane of a motoneurone in which an EPSP is evoked is known, the time course of the current generating the observed potential change can be calculated (Coombs, Curtis, and Eccles, 1956; Curtis and Eccles, 1959). Such a calculation has been made for an EPSP in a motoneurone with a time constant of 3.6 msec., resulting in a current shown by the broken line of Figure 4.6. It should be noted that the time constant of decay for the EPSP was in this instance 5 msec., and Curtis and Eccles have emphasized that invariably the constant for decay of excitatory potentials is greater than that of the membrane. This statement is applicable also to EPSP's evoked in other neurones (see Tables III and IV).

Figure 4.6 shows that the current flowing during the EPSP has a sharp rising phase lasting about 0.5 msec. Thereafter, it declines rapidly in another 1 msec., but there is still a small residuum of current evident many msec. after the initial onset. The direction of current flow, as indicated by the inset of Figure 4.6, is inward through the activated subsynaptic regions and outward through the rest of the neuronal membrane. The initial rapid phase of current flow must be correlated to the effect of the released transmitter substance which, having diffused across the cleft, has brought about the activation of the subsynaptic membrane; while the sharp drop in the current, conversely, is due to inactivation of the transmitter. The small residuum of current which persists beyond this time must be due to a prolongation of transmitter action—whether

due to continuing release of small quantities of transmitter from the presynaptic endings or to a delayed inactivation at the postsynaptic side of the last traces liberated initially is not known. It is this phase of continuing low but significant transmitter activity that accounts for the slow decay of the EPSP in motoneurones, and in other nerve cells as well. This point of view has been disputed by Rall (1959, 1960, 1962), who has sought to show that the membrane time constants measured as described above do not give a valid picture of the conductance of an electric current in the dendritic system of the neurone, and that if allowance is made for this the discrepancy between membrane time constant and time constant of decay of the EPSP disappears. According to Rall, there is therefore no need to postulate a prolonged period of transmitter action. It would appear however that Rall's objections are not justified (Eccles, 1961a), and in view of the fact that other neurones which have no dendrites and to which the uncertainties of measurement therefore do not apply show the same discrepancy, the prolonged transmitter action may be taken as a characteristic of excitatory synapses, with which the behavior at inhibitory synapses (p. 43) may be contrasted.

Information regarding the ions responsible for carrying the current flowing during the EPSP may be obtained from experiments in which the resting level of the membrane potential is altered (Coombs, Eccles, and Fatt, 1955c). Again a double-barreled microelectrode can be used, one barrel for the passage of a steady current either to depolarize or to hyperpolarize the membrane, and the second to record the evoked EPSP. Figure 4.7 illustrates a typical result in a motoneurone whose resting potential initially was –66 mV. The maximum rate of rise of the EPSP, which is related to the current flow, increases as the membrane potential is raised and falls as it is lowered, showing a reversal of polarity at about 0 mV resting potential (Figure 4.8). If the polarity of the charge across the resting membrane is changed, i.e., so that it is positive internally, the evoked EPSP also shows a reversed sign. The inference to be drawn from these observations is that the current which flows during the EPSP tends to drive the potential across the neuronal membrane to zero, i.e., the equilibrium potential for the process (E_{EPSP}) is 0 mV. This result would be obtained if the action of the transmitter substance released at the activated synapses was

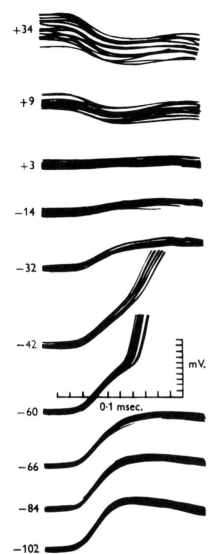

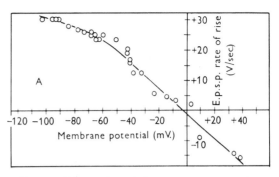

Figure 4.8. A plot of the maximum rate of rise of the EPSP against the initial level of the resting potential; data from the same cell as those of Figure 4.7. Reversal of the polarity of the EPSP again is seen to occur at a membrane potential near 0 mV. (From Coombs, Eccles, and Fatt, 1955c, by permission of the Journal of Physiology.)

Figure 4.7. EPSP's recorded from a biceps-semi-tendinosus motoneurone whose resting potential was –66 mV, evoked by afferent volleys of constant intensity. By passing current through the second barrel of a double electrode, the membrane potential was changed to the other levels indicated to the left of the figure. Depolarization of the cell reduced the amplitude of the EPSP with reversal of its sign near +3 mV; hyperpolarization increased it. (From Coombs, Eccles, and Fatt, 1955c, by permission of the Journal of Physiology.)

to cause a temporary complete breakdown in the permeability of the membrane, such that all ionic species were free to move according to their concentration gradients.

A microelectrode may also be used effectively to make a microinjection of a charged particle into a cell. Thus, for example, the passage of a hyperpolarizing current of 5×10^{-9} amp. for 60 sec. through an intracellular electrode filled with KCl solution will mean

that about 3 pequiv. of chloride ion will have passed into the cell. Assuming no restorative process during the current flow, this "injection" will rather more than double the internal chloride concentration. By the use of electrodes filled with a variety of salt solutions and appropriately polarized currents, the ionic constituents of the cellular cytoplasm can be appreciably modified, relative changes in concentration being, of course, more easily achieved for those ions normally present in the interior only in low concentration. The concentrations of a number of the cytoplasmic ions have been changed in this way, and any effect upon an evoked EPSP observed. Those ions which have been tested are chloride, nitrate, glutamate, sulphate, phosphate, potassium, and sodium, but none was found to affect the EPSP evoked in the cell (Coombs, Eccles, and Fatt, 1955c). This result is in accord with the above suggestion that the activated synapses are completely permeable to all ions within or in the environment of the cell. A number of "foreign" ions (choline, tetramethylammonium, or thiocyanate) also were without effect upon the synaptic potential, confirming the same hypothesis. The concept that the subsynaptic membrane at excitatory synapses upon motoneurones is converted into a short circuit during the action of the transmitter may therefore be fully accepted.

The results discussed above have related only to the synaptic actions of Ia fibers upon motoneurones, i.e., those involved in pathways in which no interneurone is interposed between the endings of the primary afferent axons and the motoneurone. Although excitatory activation of motoneurones from other afferent sources has been less well studied, the disynaptic excitation from group Ib fibers (involving a synaptic connection in the ipsilateral intermediate nucleus of Cajal), for example, can also be shown to result in EPSP's in motoneurones (Eccles, Fatt, Landgren, and Winsbury, 1954). In view of the great similarities between the mechanisms here described and those occurring at a wide variety of other synapses (see Chapter 5), the probability is that all excitatory processes at motoneurones have a similar mechanism.

THE RELATIONSHIP OF THE EPSP TO THE ACTION POTENTIAL

When a single nerve fiber is stimulated electrically, its response is of an all-or-nothing character, and it is well known that this is the nature also of the impulse which physiologically is caused to be conducted from the nerve cell to the terminations of its axon. We have seen above that the EPSP is not of this all-or-nothing nature, but that it exhibits a larger amplitude as the intensity of the applied presynaptic excitation is raised. We must therefore consider the manner in which the graded EPSP is transformed into an all-or-nothing action potential.

It was early evident that when an EPSP of sufficient amplitude was produced, the cell responded by an action potential which arose from the top of the EPSP. This fact is demonstrated in Figure 4.9, where it is seen that increasing the strength of presynaptic stimulation from a subthreshold value (in A), first yields a spike (in B), and that further increases result in spikes which are progressively earlier (C and D). The EPSP, then, must reach a certain level before an action potential can be generated in the cell, and the amount of presynaptic activation determines not only whether a discharge will occur, but also how early relative to the start of the EPSP it will be produced. The same effect can be shown if, in the presence of a constant EPSP, a depolarizing current is applied to the cell (through the second barrel of a double-barreled microelectrode), as in Figure 4.9, E to H. Here again the impulse generation occurs earlier as the "artificially" applied depolarization is raised. The EPSP's due to summed synaptic action thus must produce a certain degree of depolarization of the cell soma before an action potential occurs. This threshold level for discharge varies from 5 to 18 mV (average 10.6 mV) (Coombs, Curtis, and Eccles, 1957).

The threshold may also be attained by the interaction of successive EPSP's. Since these potentials are graded in nature, they may sum

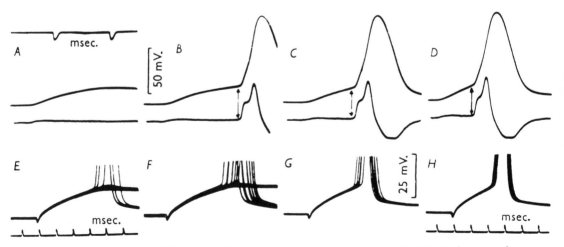

Figure 4.9. Intracellular potentials of a gastrocnemius motoneurone. In A to D, the strength of the monosynaptic activation was increased, such that A shows only an EPSP and B to D, EPSP's of progressively steeper rates of rise and action potentials appearing progressively earlier. The lower records in each case are electrically differentiated. In E to H, the monosynaptic activation was held constant, and prolonged depolarizing current pulses of increasing intensity were applied through a second electrode barrel. Again the action potentials appear progressively earlier as the rate of the slow depolarization is increased by this means. (From Coombs, Curtis, and Eccles, 1957, by permission of the Journal of Physiology.)

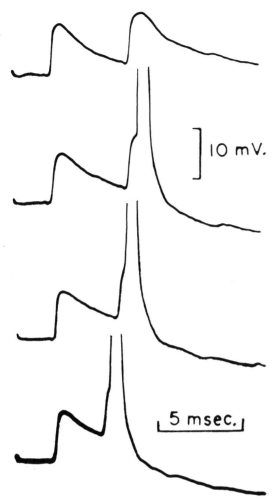

Figure 4.10. Intracellular potentials recorded from a biceps-semitendinosus motoneurone set up by two volleys of progressively decreasing interval in the afferent fibers of the biceps-semitendinosus nerve. Temporal summation of the EPSP's, giving rise to an action potential, in all but the longest volley interval. (From Eccles, 1957, by permission of Johns Hopkins Press.)

with one another; and if the interval between them is sufficiently close, an action potential may be generated by the combination of two subliminal EPSP's. An example of this is shown in Figure 4.10. This observation provides a suitable explanation of the observed reflex phenomenon of temporal facilitation (Lloyd, 1946a).

It is well recognized also that the rising phase of a motoneuronal action potential exhibits upon it a notch which can be clearly seen in the electrically differentiated records of Figure 4.9, *B* to *D*. This notch is also seen to occur following antidromic activation of motoneurones, and is therefore a characteristic of the development of an action potential in these cells. There is evidence that the notch is to be related to the discharge of the initial segment of the neurone, i.e., to the axon hillock and to the non-myelinated zone of the axon itself. The second, later and larger segment of the complex action potential results from the depolarization by the initial segment spike of the remainder of the somadendritic membrane.

For this sequence of events to occur, the initial segment must have a lower threshold for excitation than does the rest of the cellular membrane; and the currents generated at the activated synapses must flow electrotonically toward this region. The threshold for orthodromic excitation of the somadendritic membrane of normal motoneurones is on the average 25 mV (Coombs, Curtis, and Eccles, 1957), and the same value is also obtained when activation is produced by antidromic stimulation (average 26 mV). The somadendritic membrane thus has a threshold two to three times higher in motoneurones than does that of the initial segment. The same separation is observed also at other neurones of the spinal cord, e.g., the cells of the dorsal horn with which large cutaneous afferent fibers make contact (Eccles, Eccles, and Lundberg, 1960; Kostiuk, 1960); but at some, e.g., the intermediate nucleus neurones receiving Ia and Ib afferents (Eccles, Eccles, and Lundberg, 1960), there is no sign of an initial segment-somadendritic separation.

It is of some interest to inquire into a possible explanation for the lower threshold of the initial segment as compared with the remainder of the membrane. It was noted above that this region of the cell is comparatively or completely free of synaptic endings, while a large proportion of the remainder of the soma and of the proximal dendrites are thickly covered with boutons. The suggestion has been put forward that the lower threshold is causally related to this morphological observation. Although this is a possibility for consideration for motoneurones, it cannot explain the lesser excitability of the somal compared with the axonal membranes of the giant ganglion cells of *Aplysia* (Tauc, 1960b) or of the spinal ganglion cells of frogs (Ito, 1957). In both these cases, the somata of the cells are completely free of synaptic endings, which are confined to the axons at some distance from the cell bodies.

The hypothesis that the extent of synaptic coverage of a cell could affect the threshold for excitation derives from the finding that some subsynaptic membranes which respond by the generation of postsynaptic potentials under the influence of an appropriate transmitter substance appear to be electrically inexcitable, i.e., they do not respond by a large and specific increase in sodium conductance when subjected to an electrical depolarization. A specific conductance change of this type, which occurs during the rising phase of an action potential, can be regarded as a criterion of electrical excitability. Such behavior has been demonstrated, for example, in the tonic muscles of amphibia (Burke and Ginsborg, 1956); for the electric organs of a number of fish (for references see Grundfest, 1957); and for lobster cardiac ganglion cells (Hagiwara, Watanabe, and Saito, 1959). On the basis of these specific instances, Grundfest has argued that *all* subsynaptic membranes are electrically inexcitable, and therefore, to return to the case of the motoneurone, that since four-fifths of the somadendritic portion of its surface can be subsynaptic, its threshold for electrical excitation would be high. However, it is certain that in some cases both chemical and electrical excitability are not mutually exclusive, as for example in crustacean muscle fibers (Hoyle and Wiersma, 1958a) or in denervated mammalian skeletal muscle (Axelsson and Thesleff, 1959). It is not possible to demonstrate directly whether an increased sodium conductance in response to electrical stimulation can occur at the subsynaptic membranes of motoneurones, but in view of the fact that both electrical and chemical excitability can be observed together in other situations and that some cells without synaptic investment also have a low excitability, this explanation for the lower threshold for excitation of the initial segment membrane becomes considerably less attractive.

Nevertheless, the difference in threshold is a fact and must have an explanation. Terzuolo and Araki (1961) provided evidence that the membrane conductance of the somadendritic section rises only to about one-fourth that of an active axonal membrane. Even if the suggestion of electrical inexcitability of the subsynaptic areas cannot be accepted, the fact is that much of the membrane is covered both by boutons and by closely applied glial elements, and therefore that the extracellular space surrounding it is very restricted. This will tend to reduce the extent of any conductance changes and thus the electrical excitability of the membrane. In view of the findings in cells which do not have a dense synaptic coverage of their somata but which are infolded by Schwann cells, this is perhaps a more acceptable explanation of the observed facts.

Purpura and Grundfest (1956) have claimed that the apical dendrites of cortical pyramidal cells and, by extension, the dendrites of all neurones are also electrically inexcitable. This point of view is not accepted by others (Eccles, 1961b), and the results observed are capable of other interpretations. Nevertheless, it is true that the threshold for the excitation of dendrites is high, and that there is a high possibility for impulse blockage during conduction along them. It has been remarked above that the effectiveness of synaptic junctions situated far out upon the dendrites of motoneurones is small because of the length constant of the system, and the implication that there is a functional significance to the unfavorable position in this respect of the posterior root synapses at frogs' motoneurones (Fadiga and Brookhart, 1960) or of contralateral connections in mammalian cells (Sprague, 1958) is worthy of note. Since there must be electrotonic spread of current from the activated synapses to the initial segment in order for activation of the neurone to occur, the distance of the posterior root endings from this region compared to that of the lateral column synapses will markedly reduce their effectiveness.

Although, as indicated here and further discussed below, there are marked similarities between synaptic mechanisms at various types of neurones, the responses of the postsynaptic cells are very variable. Thus, on the one hand, motoneurones usually respond by a single action potential to threshold orthodromic excitation, while on the other hand some spinal interneurones may fire repetitively at rates in excess of 1000/sec. This difference is in part related to the degree and time course of the membrane hyperpolarization which follows the production of an action potential. In typical motoneurones the somadendritic spike declines slowly for several msecs. and reverses into a hyperpolarization which has a maximum amplitude of about 5 mV at 5 to 10 msec. and thereafter slowly declines for about 100 msec. (Coombs, Eccles, and Fatt, 1955a; Kostiuk, 1960) (Figure 4.11 at 76 mV). Passage of currents through the cell indicates that the equilibrium potential for the process is close to –90 mV (Figures 4.11 and 4.12), which is approximately that of the equilibrium potential for potassium ions (Coombs, Eccles, and Fatt, 1955a; Kuno, 1959). Changes in

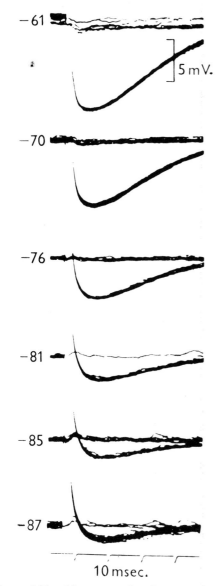

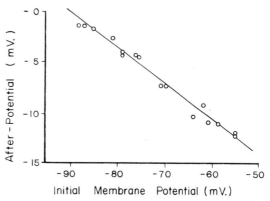

Figure 4.12. A plot of the peak amplitude of the after-potential against membrane potential; data from the same motoneurone as in Figure 4.11. The equilibrium potential for the process is seen to be about –90 mV. (From Coombs, Eccles, and Fatt, 1955a, by permission of the Journal of Physiology.)

Figure 4.11. After-potentials of a motoneurone, recorded at various levels of the membrane potential, which was set by the application of a polarizing current applied through one barrel of a double electrode. The resting potential of the cell was about –76 mV. Hyperpolarization resulted in a decreased, and depolarization in an increased, amplitude of the after-potential. (From Coombs, Eccles, and Fatt, 1955a, by permission of the Journal of Physiology.)

the intracellular composition confirm that the after-hyperpolarization is probably entirely due to an increased outward flux of potassium ions. In contrast to this, the after-hyperpolarization in interneurones either is very brief or is not observable at all (Hunt and Kuno, 1959); and since the after-hyperpolarization imposes upon the cell a period of relative refractoriness, the duration of this potential change will exert a degree of control upon the rate of repetitive discharge in the presence of a constant level of synaptic depolarization.

Since neurones in general are activated by repetitive volleys in the presynaptic terminals making synaptic contact with them, the question of the repetitive activation and activity of such cells is clearly of fundamental physiological importance. An investigation of repetitive synaptic action can best be carried out by observation of EPSP's with intracellular electrodes, although much earlier information was obtained with observations of reflex responses and of electrotonically conducted postsynaptic potentials (for references see Curtis and Eccles, 1960).

If the amplitudes of EPSP's produced monosynaptically in a motoneurone at various rates of stimulation are observed, it is found that their size varies with the frequency (Figure 4.13). At low stimulus frequencies, the EPSP's are found to be of approximately the same amplitude, but if evoked at rates above 1/sec. they are depressed, becoming minimal at 5 to 10/sec. With a further increase in frequency, the EPSP's increase to a maximum amplitude at about 70/sec., and again decline at rates in excess of 100/sec. This observation provides an explanation for the change with stimulation rate in reflex spike height (Lloyd and Wilson, 1957) and in the response of single motoneurones (Lloyd, 1957).

It is of some interest to assess this dependency of the EPSP upon presynaptic frequency of stimulation in terms of synaptic efficiency,

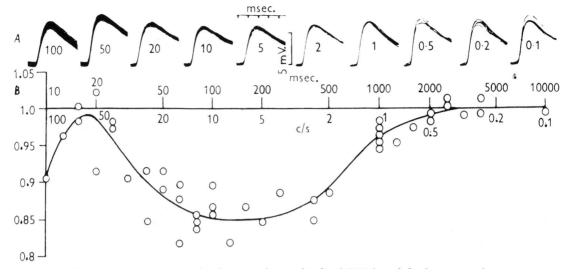

Figure 4.13. The relationship between the amplitude of EPSP's and the frequency of stimulation in a biceps-semitendinosus motoneurone with a resting potential of –62 mV. *A*, The EPSP's observed at the frequencies indicated; *B*, a plot of the amplitudes as a fraction of that at 0.4 c/sec. against the stimulus frequency on a logarithmic abscissal scale. Above the frequency scale the stimulus intervals in msec. are shown. (From Curtis and Eccles, 1960, by permission of the Journal of Physiology.)

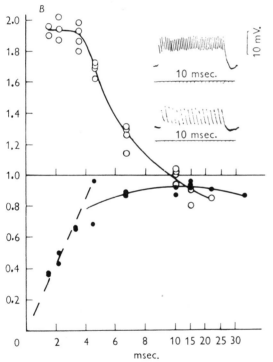

Figure 4.14. EPSP's were evoked in a gastrocnemius motoneurone with a resting potential of –68 mV. •: sizes of the last response of a repetitive series relative to the size of an EPSP obtained after a rest period, plotted against the stimulus interval in msec. (logarithmic scale). The straight line through the origin indicates a direct proportionality at high frequencies. ○: a plot of the plateau height against the stimulus interval. The attainment of a maximum rate of output of transmitter is indicated by the flattening of the curve at frequencies between 300 and 600/sec. The inset shows records obtained at 150 and 300/sec. (From Curtis and Eccles, 1960, by permission of the Journal of Physiology.)

i.e., with the total amount of transmitter substance liberated per unit time. An estimate of this may be obtained by multiplying the observed height of the EPSP by the interval between stimuli, and the result is the curve of Figure 4.14. It is clear that the total amount of transmitter liberated in unit time rises to a maximum when the frequency is about 300/sec. and thereafter remains constant. The questions relating to the mobilization and liberation of transmitter inherent in these observations have been discussed in Chapter 3.

THE INHIBITORY POSTSYNAPTIC POTENTIAL

The earliest demonstrations of the nervous inhibition of a target organ were those which followed stimulation of a peripheral nerve, and of these the first to be described was the action of the vagus on the heart (Volkmann, 1838; Weber and Weber, 1845). In 1887 Gaskell reported the hyperpolarization of heart muscle during this inhibition, an electrical change which is now recognized as a characteristic of many such processes. In the central nervous system the earliest observation was by Sechenov (1863), who showed an inhibition of spinal reflex activity following the application of salt crystals to the midbrain of a frog. To cover all the multitude of

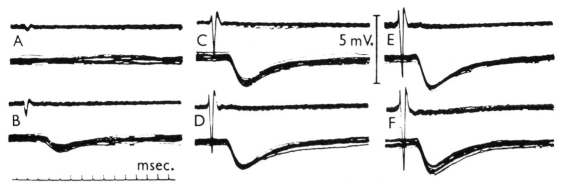

Figure 4.15. IPSP's recorded in a biceps-semitendinosus motoneurone in response to increasing strengths of afferent stimulation, indicated by the upper traces in each record, applied to the quadriceps nerve. The amplitude of the IPSP increases with the strength of the afferent volley, while its time course is unaffected. (From Coombs, Eccles, and Fatt, 1955d, by permission of the Journal of Physiology.)

experimental observations which has accrued in the century since Sechenov's work, Eccles (1961b) has defined nervous inhibition as follows: "Nerve impulses exert an inhibitory action when they cause a depression of the generation of impulses by a nerve or muscle cell, which is attributable to a specific physiological process and which does not arise as a consequence of its previous activation."

Again the use of microelectrode techniques has made possible the elucidation of inhibitory processes within the spinal cord, and full explanations for the inhibitions of monosynaptic reflex activity earlier described by Renshaw (1941, 1942) and by Lloyd (1941, 1946a,b) are now available. Stimulation of a group Ia afferent pathway in an antagonistic muscle nerve results in the development of a transmembrane potential change leading to the hyperpolarization of the protagonist motoneurone. This potential, like the EPSP, is generated by the postsynaptic neurone, and is not a passive consequence of an applied external electrical field (Brock, Coombs, and Eccles, 1952; Eccles, Fatt, and Koketsu, 1954; Coombs, Eccles, and Fatt, 1955b). Coombs, Eccles, and Fatt (1955b) have named this potential change the "inhibitory postsynaptic potential" (IPSP).

As is to be expected, IPSP's recorded from mammalian motoneurones are similar in many respects to EPSP's. Again the amplitude of the potential change is graded, increasing with the intensity of the applied stimulation (Figure 4.15). The hyperpolarization is first observable about 1.5 msec. after the entry of the afferent volley into the cord; thereafter it rises to a summit in a further 1.5 to 2.0 msec.,

and decays with an exponential time course having an average time constant of 3.3 msec. (Coombs, Eccles, and Fatt, 1955d; Curtis and Eccles, 1959). It thus differs from the EPSP only in that its latency of onset is longer and time constant of decay shorter.

The longer latency may be correlated in part to a greater conduction distance within the cord, but when allowance is made for this, the minimum additional time for onset of the inhibitory, as contrasted with the excitatory, potential is 0.8 msec. (Eccles, Fatt, and Landgren, 1956; Curtis, Krnjević, and Miledi, 1958), while the actual delay at the synapse has been shown directly in each case to be about 0.5 msec. (Eide, Lundberg, and Voorhoeve, 1961). The suggestion was therefore made that an interneurone was interposed in this "direct" inhibitory pathway, which in effect transformed the excitatory synaptic action of Ia afferent endings into an inhibitory one upon the motoneurones (see Table I). Electrophysiological evidence for the existence of these neurones in the intermediate nucleus of Cajal of the cord has been obtained (Eccles, Fatt, and Landgren, 1956; Curtis, Krnjević, and Miledi, 1958; Eccles, Eccles, and Lundberg, 1960), and anatomically the axons of the interneurones have been shown to terminate on motoneurones (Szentágothai, 1951). These cells respond to Ia activation by the production of typical EPSP's and show the necessarily brief synaptic delay (Araki, Eccles, and Ito, 1960). The direct inhibition of motoneurones by stimulation of fibers from antagonistic muscles is thus mediated through a disynaptic arc, with the additional delay at the Ia-interneurone synapse accurately accounting for the longer latency of the process.

It appears that the generation of an IPSP is a feature common to all inhibitory processes which are the result of synaptic action upon motoneurones. Those pathways which have been examined, in addition to the direct inhibition by antagonistic Ia fibers, are the inhibitions from Ib and III muscle afferents, from cutaneous impulses, from impulses in motor axon collaterals and from pyramidal tract fibers. The Ib and motor axon collateral inhibitions (Coombs, Eccles, and Fatt, 1955b; Eccles, Eccles, and Lundberg, 1957, 1960) and that from the pyramidal tract (Preston and Whitlock, 1960) are all mediated by disynaptic pathways in which the excitatory fibers end upon inhibitory interneurones, these in turn making contact with the motoneurones. For the Ib pathways these interneurones also lie in the intermediate nucleus of the cord. The motor axon collaterals are joined synaptically to small cells in the anterior horn of the cord which have been named Renshaw cells (Eccles, Fatt, and Koketsu, 1954) after the discoverer of their characteristic activity (Renshaw, 1946). There is no indication of the existence within the central nervous system of a neurone which possesses excitatory actions at one set of endings and inhibitory ones at another, i.e., for the same chemical transmitter substance exhibiting the two types of action at different sites. It is likely that the interposition of an interneurone as a commutator, transforming excitatory input to an inhibitory output, occurs in all instances.

It was mentioned above that the IPSP is also a graded response, and that therefore it represents the summed reaction of unitary potentials each having the same time course. If the change of potential with time and the time constant of the neuronal membrane are known, the time course of the current generating the observed potential change can be calculated. This generating current is shown in Figure 4.16 for a motoneurone whose resting potential was –66 mV. It is seen that its time course is very similar to that of the current generating an EPSP (cf. Figure 4.6), except that in this case there is no phase of

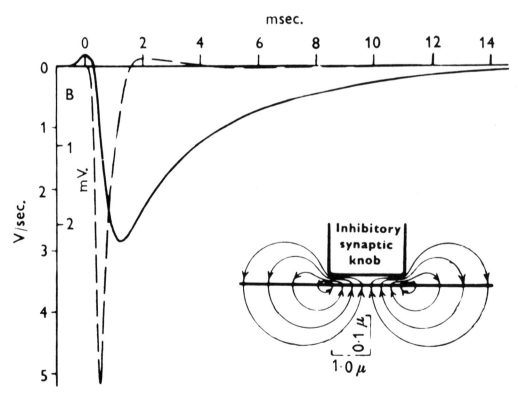

Figure 4.16.   The observed IPSP (solid line) and calculated generating current (broken line) from the same motoneurone as that of Figure 4.6, with which these curves should be compared. The inset shows the direction of current flow under an active inhibitory ending. (From Curtis and Eccles, 1959, by permission of the Journal of Physiology.)

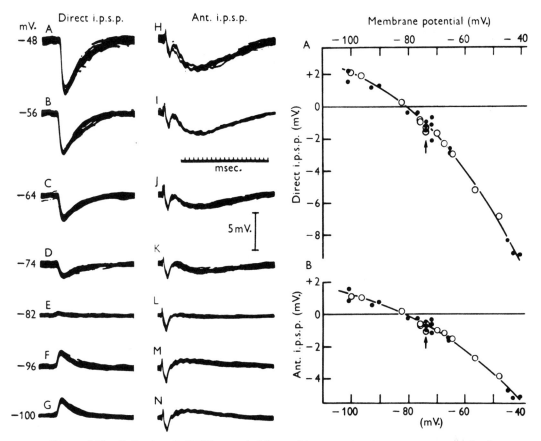

Figure 4.17. Left: *A* to *G*, IPSP's recorded from a biceps-semitendinosus motoneurone by the direct inhibitory action of group Ia afferents in quadriceps nerve; *H* to *N*, antidromic IPSP's set up by Renshaw cell activation following stimulation of the anterior roots. The initial diphasic spike in these is the field potential produced by the antidromic invasion of adjacent motoneurones. The initial resting potential was –74 mV, and this was changed by the application of current. For both sets of records the IPSP shows reversal of polarity at about –80 mV. Right: plots of the maximum amplitudes of the IPSP's against membrane potential for (*A*) direct inhibition and (*B*) antidromic inhibition, both before (●) and after (○) the passage of a depolarizing current 9 minutes previously. Note the increased amplitude of the responses during depolarization, reversal at about –80 mV, and depolarizing IPSP's at high levels of the membrane potential. (From Coombs, Eccles, and Fatt, 1955b, by permission of the Journal of Physiology.)

prolonged transmitter action and the current falls swiftly to zero or is transiently reversed. The effect of this is that the time constant for decay of the IPSP is only slightly longer than that of the neuronal membrane (3.3 msec. versus 2.9 msec., on the average), and this observation has been made for all motoneurones investigated. The second point of difference between excitatory and inhibitory potentials can therefore be explained in terms of a decreased time of residual transmitter action. The inset of Figure 4.16 shows the direction of current flow during activity at an inhibitory synapse: outward through the active subsynaptic membrane and inward through the rest of the cell surface.

Using double-barreled microelectrodes, experiments have been carried out to determine the equilibrium potential for the IPSP by observing its polarity and amplitude at various levels of the membrane potential. Figure 4.17 indicates the results obtained in a motoneurone whose resting potential was –74 mV for inhibitory potentials generated by antagonistic Ia volleys (direct IPSP) and for those resulting from antidromic volleys in the motor roots (ant. IPSP). The changes obtained are essentially identical for the two series. As the membrane was depolarized from the resting level, the IPSP became larger; hyperpolarization resulted in a smaller evoked potential change which showed a reversal of polarity at about –82 mV. In a number of similar experiments, Coombs, Eccles, and Fatt (1955b) showed that the average equilibrium potential for the IPSP was about –80 mV.

The nature of the ions contributing to the IPSP is difficult to decide. In the original work of Coombs, Eccles, and Fatt (1955b), recently extended by Araki, Ito, and Oscarsson (1961), it was shown that the injection of chloride ions into the postsynaptic cell by the passage of an appropriately directed current would change the hyperpolarization into a depolarizing response. The latter authors have shown that a number of other anions, all of hydrated radius less than 1.32 times that of the potassium ion, could substitute for chloride in this respect, while larger ions were ineffective. The simplest explanation of these results is that the action of the inhibitory transmitter substance is to open pores in the subsynaptic membrane of a rigidly fixed size, such that only ions with radius less than 5 Å can pass. Chloride is the only intracellular anion of these dimensions present in sufficient concentration to be able to contribute to the potential, and movement of this ion down its concentration gradient would yield a hyperpolarization of the cell. During chloride injection, the gradient could be reversed such that activation would now give rise to a net outward movement and depolarization.

However, we have seen that the equilibrium potential for chloride ions is about –70 mV, whereas E_{IPSP} is about –80 mV; and if chloride were the only ion contributing to the IPSP, then E_{Cl} should be approximately the same as E_{IPSP}. Two possibilities present themselves, either: (a) some other ion contributes to the IPSP or (b) an active transport mechanism for chloride exists in motoneurones such that E_{Cl} is kept at 10 mV more depolarization than the resting potential, in the same way that E_K is held at 20 mV more depolarization (see p. 29). There is, however, no evidence from studies of other tissues that such a chloride pump exists (cf. Hodgkin and Horowicz, 1959; Adrian, 1960).

If attention is directed to the possible contribution of the cations to the IPSP, it is clear that only the efflux of potassium from the cell would give rise to a hyperpolarization. Sodium ions must therefore be rigidly excluded from participation in any permeability changes, and since their radius is 1.45 times that of potassium, this could be explained on the basis of the size of the opened pores in the subsynaptic membrane. In the original experiments of Coombs, Eccles, and Fatt (1955b), it was felt that the movement of potassium was probably as important as that of chloride during the IPSP, but the results obtained following intracellular injections of sodium or potassium were somewhat equivocal (for a full discussion of this question see Eccles [1961b]). The upshot is that movement of chloride ions would appear able to account completely for the generation of the IPSP except for the requirement for an active transport mechanism for these ions. To eliminate the necessity of this postulated chloride pump, for which there is no other experimental evidence, a minor role for potassium has been suggested, in spite of the unsatisfactory nature of the experiments designed to test this hypothesis. Eccles has suggested that the relative contribution of chloride to potassium during the generation of the inhibitory current might be in the proportion of 4 to 1.

The decision cannot be helped by considering inhibitory processes in other situations, for all possibilities have been demonstrated. Thus, the vagal inhibition of heart muscle is due to a hyperpolarization resulting from increased potassium permeability only (Trautwein, Kuffler, and Edwards, 1956); the inhibition of crustacean muscle to increased chloride permeability only (Boistel and Fatt, 1958); and that of *Aplysia* ganglion cells, like the motoneurone, probably to the movement of both potassium and chloride (Tauc, 1958).

The interaction of excitatory and inhibitory postsynaptic potentials has been studied by Curtis and Eccles (1959), and is illustrated by Figure 4.18, in which the interval between the two stimuli has been varied. It is clear that a considerable diminution in amplitude of the excitatory potential can be obtained (as in G), or that its duration is severely curtailed (as in J). Combinations of these two influences occur at intermediate intervals.

There are two factors operating here which tend to depress the EPSP. Simultaneous activation of both types of synapse gives rise to electrotonically conducted currents flowing from the synaptic regions toward the initial segment which are oppositely directed and therefore will tend to neutralize one another. This antagonism clearly will result in the lessened effectiveness of the excitatory volley; if this had previously been liminal for the generation of an action potential, it will be subthreshold during the operation of the inhibitory synapses and the neurone therefore is effectively blocked.

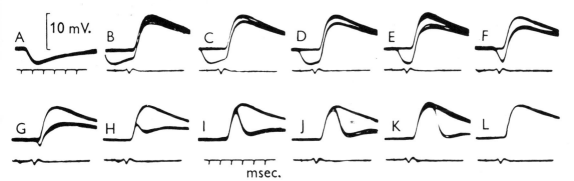

Figure 4.18. The interaction of excitatory and inhibitory PSP's in a biceps-semitendinosus motoneurone with resting potential –70 mV. IPSP's were evoked by Ia afferents in the quadriceps nerve and EPSP's from the biceps-semitendinosus nerve. Control IPSP in *A*, EPSP in *L*. In *B* to *K*, the control EPSP is also shown as the upper curve of the superimposed traces, since the inhibitory stimulation was turned on only for one-half of the sweeps. The intervals between the two stimuli were varied, showing the different types of reduction of excitatory input that can be brought about by the inhibitory volleys. (From Curtis and Eccles, 1959, by permission of the Journal of Physiology.)

The second influence is the action of the membrane hyperpolarization resulting from the inhibitory current flow. If experiments are

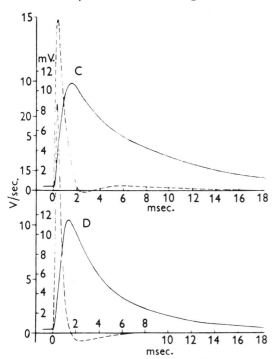

Figure 4.19. The effect of a hyperpolarizing current on the EPSP of a gastrocnemius motoneurone, resting potential –74 mV. The solid lines are the observed EPSP's, the broken lines the calculated generating currents; above, control; below, during passage of a current of 8×10^{-9} amp. Note the sharper rising phase and faster decay of the EPSP and the disappearance of the residual excitatory current during hyperpolarization of the cell. (From Curtis and Eccles, 1959, by permission of the Journal of Physiology.)

carried out in which a steady hyperpolarizing current is applied across the neuronal membrane, it is found that the EPSP has a sharper rising phase and larger amplitude (Figure 4.19 and also Figure 4.7; Coombs, Eccles, and Fatt, 1955c; Curtis and Eccles, 1959), but also decays with a shorter time constant. This is due to elimination of the residual phase of the excitatory transmitter action, and thus the effectiveness of the EPSP in a temporal sense is depressed. Both these effects may be expected to occur during a physiologically evoked IPSP, and the balance of excitatory and inhibitory influences, considered from moment to moment, are able very finely to control the activity of the motoneurone.

The time course of the IPSP elicited in motoneurones by stimulation of pathways other than the Ia afferent is frequently prolonged (Eccles, Eccles, and Lundberg, 1957; Eccles and Lundberg, 1959). This effect is much more noticeable with the inhibition produced by antidromic stimulation of the motor axons (Eccles, Fatt, and Koketsu, 1954), and would appear in this instance to be completely explained by the repetitive discharge of the inhibitory interneurones involved in this particular pathway. Mention has already been made of the discovery by Renshaw of the prolonged inhibition of motoneuronal discharge subsequent to an antidromic volley in the motor axons, and of the identification of the small cells within the anterior horn which have been given his name as the interneurones responsible for the inhibition (Eccles, Fatt, and Koketsu, 1954). These cells have been

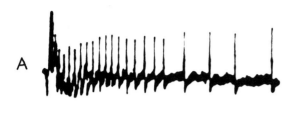

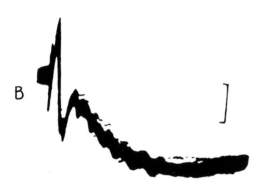

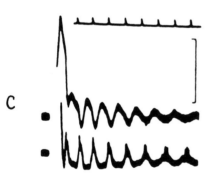

Figure 4.20. Records illustrating the effects of Renshaw cell activation. *A,* The typical discharge pattern of a Renshaw cell in response to a single antidromic volley in a motor nerve. Note the high initial frequency of discharge. Duration of sweep, 45 msec. *B,* Maximal IPSP recorded from a deep peroneal motoneurone brought about by antidromic stimulation. Note the "ripple" upon the IPSP, reflecting the repetitive discharge of the Renshaw cells. Voltage calibration, 1 mV; duration of sweep, 14 msec. The ripple is seen also in *C* recorded from the dorsolateral surface of the cord (above) and from the vicinity of a Renshaw cell (below). Voltage calibrations 0.1 mV for upper and 1 mV for lower traces; time marker in msec. (From Eccles, Fatt, and Koketsu, 1954, by permission of the Journal of Physiology.)

shown to produce, in response to a single volley, a long continuing burst of impulses, initially of a high frequency, which gradually subsides (Figure 4.20*A*). The initial portion of the IPSP evoked in a motoneurone by this discharge is shown in Figure 4.20*B*, and it will be noted that the IPSP shows a clear "ripple" upon it. This ripple is a reflection of the repetitive discharge of the Renshaw cells and it may be recorded even from the surface of the cord (Figure 4.20*C*). The prolonged nature of the antidromic inhibitory pathway can therefore be satisfactorily explained in terms of the discharge pattern of the inhibitory interneurones involved in it.

It is probable that a similar mechanism underlies the prolonged inhibitions brought about by other stimulations, and that all are due to repetitive activation of the inhibitory synapses rather than to a persistent action of transmitter released by a single incoming volley.

PRESYNAPTIC INHIBITION

The action of the alkaloid strychnine upon the spinal cord has been recognized for many years (Magendie, 1807), but it is much more recently that the specific effect of low doses of this drug in blocking inhibitory synaptic action has become known. The action of such small doses of strychnine in preventing some reflex inhibitory processes was shown originally by Sherrington (1905); however, Liddell and Sherrington (1925) also observed that there were some spinal inhibitory mechanisms which were resistant to strychnine. Since all postsynaptic inhibitory processes in mammals have been found to be prevented by the drug, the explanation for these discrepancies has, until lately, been obscure. Whether such other reflex inhibitions in higher centers which are not prevented by strychnine, as, for example, those of the tonic neck and labyrinthine reflexes (Magnus and Wolf, 1913), are analogous is not yet known.

The electrical recording of the strychnine-resistant inhibition in motoneurones was first made by Frank and Fuortes (1957) and by Frank (1959). They showed that Ia afferent volleys could reduce the size of a monosynaptically evoked EPSP without there being any other sign of an effect upon the postsynaptic neurone. There was no change in the membrane potential similar to that brought about by the IPSP, either at the level of the resting potential or when this was displaced by the application of a depolarizing or a hyperpolarizing current. Further, the excitability of the neurone, as tested by antidromic invasion or by the threshold depolarization required for generation of an impulse, was unchanged. Frank (1959) considered that the inhibition of the EPSP might be due to processes occurring far out upon the dendrites of the motoneurone, such that no trace of the inhibitory action itself could be detected in records made from the cell soma; and he named the phenomenon, in consequence, "remote inhibition." The mechanism underlying remote inhibition has been studied by Eccles and his colleagues, who have been able to show that in all probability the presynaptic terminals of the excitatory axons are the site of the effect, and they have therefore returned to it the more descriptive title of "presynaptic inhibition," which was originally used by Frank and Fuortes.

Briefly, the characteristics of presynaptic inhibitory action are these. It is a very long-lasting effect, noticeable at a testing interval as short as 2.5 msec. and with a maximum at 10 to 20 msec., but observable even after 200 msec. It is potentiated by a lower body temperature and enormously so by a brief repetitive stimulus to the inhibitory fibers. It was reported to be most strikingly produced by Ia and Ib afferent impulses from flexor muscles, especially in extensor motoneurones, and little, if at all, by group II or III impulses (Eccles, Eccles, and Magni, 1961; Eccles, Schmidt, and Willis, 1962). There is an increasing body of evidence, however, that all afferent impulses entering the cord may exert a presynaptic inhibitory influence (Eccles, Kostyuk, and Schmidt, 1962a,b). A typical series of EPSP's in a gastrocnemius motoneurone, depressed by maximal group I volleys in the posterior biceps-semitendinosus nerve, together with the time course of the whole process, are shown in Figure 4.21. The extremely important role played by this mechanism in the regulation of spinal reflex activity, and by extension very probably of other central nervous events as well, is emphasized in

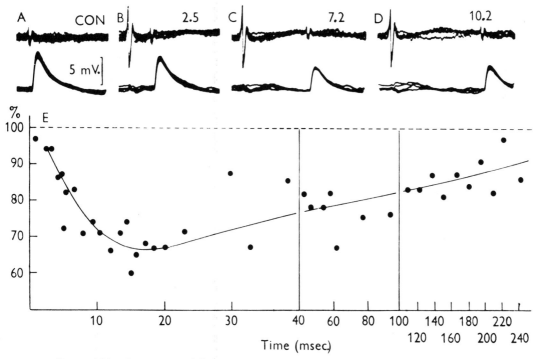

Figure 4.21. Presynaptic inhibition in a gastrocnemius motoneurone resulting from maximal group I volleys in posterior biceps-semitendinosus nerve. Monosynaptic EPSP's were evoked at various intervals after the inhibitory stimulus by maximal stimulation of gastrocnemius-soleus nerve. *A* shows the control EPSP; *B, C,* and *D*, those at the intervals marked above the records. The time course of the depress is shown in *E*, where the ordinates are the sizes of the EPSP's as percentages of the control. (From Eccles, Eccles, and Magni, 1961, by permission of the Journal of Physiology.)

the following statement made by Eccles, Eccles, and Magni (1961): "The long duration of the presynaptic inhibition produced by a single volley, gives opportunity for summation of the asynchronous discharges from muscle receptor organs; hence it would be expected that through their presynaptic inhibitory action such discharges would be very effective in depressing reflexes."

Two pieces of evidence give rise to the hypothesis that this EPSP depression is of presynaptic origin; the one negative, which is that no conductance change occurs in the postsynaptic cell, and the other that the time course of the depression can be perfectly correlated with depolarization of the presynaptic fibers, this latter being observable as the so-called dorsal root reflex in muscle afferents (Brooks and Koizumi, 1956; Eccles, Kozak, and Magni, 1961). The depression of excitatory synaptic action is in this case of double origin, thus: (a) the centrifugal dorsal root reflex impulses will collide with the afferent testing volley and reduce its effectiveness, and (b) the depolarization of the fibers, as indicated by the dorsal root reflex, will effectively reduce the output of transmitter from the terminal and thus also depress the EPSP. The parallelism between depression of the EPSP and the size of the testing volley is illustrated in Figure 4.22. The axonal depolarization has been established directly by intracellular recording from the primary afferent fibers and observation of their excitability to brief current pulses delivered in their proximity during the period of presynaptic inhibition (Eccles, Eccles, and Magni, 1960; Eccles, Magni, and

Willis, 1962). Such increased excitability gives a measure of the extent of axonal depolarization (Wall, 1958). The relationship between the size of the presynaptic impulse and the EPSP has been directly determined only for the giant synapse of the stellate ganglion of the squid (Hagiwara and Tasaki, 1958; see Figure 3-2), and there it was shown that depression of the presynaptic spike by one-fifth, through the application of a depolarizing current, almost completely abolished the postsynaptic response. At the mammalian neuromuscular junction, Liley (1956b) estimated that the output of acetylcholine was increased 10-fold for each 15 mV of presynaptic depolarization; and if the same relationship holds at motoneuronal synapses, a comparatively small change in the level of presynaptic polarization would be sufficient to reduce markedly the output of the excitatory transmitter when an impulse was delivered to the endings.

The fact that a minimal interval of about 2.5 msec. is required between excitatory and inhibitory volleys for presynaptic inhibition to be observable would appear to indicate that some type of chemical transmission process is involved and to make less likely the possibility that an electrotonic depolarization of the primary afferent fibers has occurred. A second piece of evidence substantiating this concept is the finding that, although presynaptic inhibition is not sensitive to subconvulsive doses of strychnine, it can be blocked by the convulsant agent picrotoxin (Eccles, 1962), a drug which has a powerful action in antagonizing the inhibitory transmitter at some in-

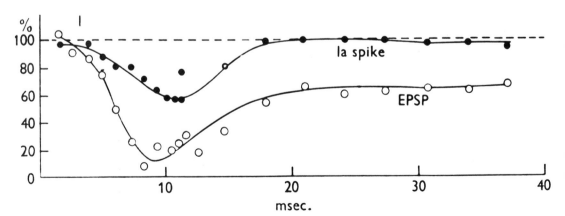

Figure 4.22. Relationship between the depression of EPSP's and depression of the testing afferent volley, plotted in each case as percentages of the control amplitudes. EPSP's were evoked in a gastrocnemius motoneurone by stimulation of gastrocnemius afferents; inhibition from preceding maximal group I volleys in posterior biceps-semitendinosus nerve. (From Eccles, Eccles, and Magni, 1961, by permission of the Journal of Physiology.)

vertebrate synapses (see p. 97). Synaptic endings must be postulated as impinging either upon the presynaptic axons or upon the terminal endings of those axons, and releasing upon them a depolarizing transmitter. There is as yet no definite anatomical evidence to substantiate this view, but the available physiological data make the existence of such structures most probable.

RECURRENT DISINHIBITION

The effect of an antidromic volley in motor axons may be, as we have seen, to give rise to recurrent inhibition of motoneurones due to excitation of the Renshaw cells. However, under some circumstances a facilitation of monosynaptic reflexes may occur following such a conditioning antidromic volley (Wilson, 1959), and this phenomenon has been shown also to be due to impulses passing in motor axon collaterals through an arc which involves more synaptic relays than does that giving rise to recurrent inhibition. This "recurrent facilitation" has been found to be reduced by the administration of tetanus toxin or strychnine to the animal, and both these agents are known specifically to affect inhibitory synapses. The suggestion was therefore put forward that recurrent facilitation in fact was the removal of a background inhibition exerted upon the motoneurone, and was not in itself an excitatory phenomenon (Wilson, Diecke, and Talbot, 1960). It is to be considered therefore as a "disinhibition" (Wilson and Burgess, 1962).

A recurrent disinhibitory volley characteristically produces a small and prolonged depolarization of the motoneuronal membrane (Figure 4.23A), which can be reversed to a hyperpolarization by the application of an hyperpolarizing current pulse (Figure 4.23B) (Wilson and Burgess, 1961). If the depolarization observed in a resting cell were due to a change in permeability of the same type as occurs during an EPSP, then hyperpolarization would not be expected to cause its reversal (see p. 34). On the other hand, if the applied hyperpolarization shifted the membrane potential such that it was more negative than E_{IPSP}, then any background inhibition would be indicated by depolarization, and release from such a background by hyperpolarization. This explanation appears to be in accord with the observed facts.

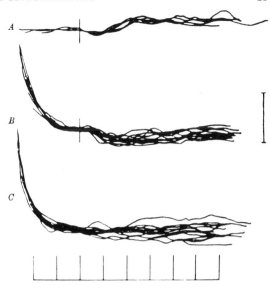

Figure 4.23. A, The recurrent disinhibitory potential recorded from a deep peroneal motoneurone, appearing as a prolonged depolarization of the cell. B shows the reversal of this potential change brought about by the application of a hyperpolarizing current; the lack of membrane potential change caused by the current alone is indicated in C. (From Wilson and Burgess, 1961, by permission of Macmillan & Co., Ltd.)

Since the long latency of recurrent disinhibition indicates the presence of several synapses in the pathway, its details are unknown. However, since agents capable of blocking inhibitory synapses are effective in reducing it, and since its equilibrium potential would seem to be near that for the IPSP, presumably the postsynaptic inhibition of an inhibitory arc is involved. If a degree of tone existed in the inhibitory arc, such that some inhibitory synapses upon the motoneurone were continually active, removal of this influence would materially affect the excitability of the cell. The process represents another way in which the activity of cells can be controlled at the spinal level.

SUMMARY

The following is a summary of the synaptic actions recognized as influencing the activity of motoneurones.

(1) Excitation is mediated by the release of a transmitter substance which affects the subsynaptic membrane in such a way as to cause a complete breakdown of its normal permeability, with the result that a current flows tending to drive the membrane poten-

tial across the neuronal surface to zero. This depolarizing current, if large enough, will trigger the postsynaptic cell to discharge an all-or-nothing action potential.

(2) Postsynaptic inhibition results from the action of an inhibitory transmitter which acts upon the appropriate subsynaptic areas in such a way as to cause them to become permeable to chloride and probably to potassium ions. The resultant current leads to the hyperpolarization of the cell membrane and thus to its relative inhibition.

(3) Recurrent disinhibition is a process which can follow activation of motoneurones, and is of a nature to reduce the extent of background inhibition, presumably through synaptic blockage of an inhibitory pathway.

(4) Presynaptic inhibition reduces the effectiveness of excitatory synapses by depolarizing and thus reducing the output of transmitter from the terminals which make contact with the motoneurones.

The postsynaptic potentials produced by various types of afferent stimulation are similar; thus, for example, both excitatory and inhibitory potentials were observed in motoneurones following stimulation of the precentral cortex which were virtually identical in character to those observed following sensory root stimulation (Preston and Whitlock, 1961). The interaction of influences arriving at a neurone from many sources is, of course, the most fundamental process which occurs within the nervous system.

Chapter 5

SYNAPTIC EVENTS
AT OTHER SITES

This chapter presents a comparatively brief survey of the details of synaptic transmission processes at sites other than the mammalian motoneurone in order to point out the many similarities and the occasional differences which occur (Table IV). It is not intended that the subjects considered here should be taken to comprise the whole body of available information on this very broad subject.

NEUROMUSCULAR JUNCTIONAL TRANSMISSION TO STRIATED MUSCLE

In point of chronology, the first investigations into synaptic events were made at vertebrate neuromuscular junctions, and information has been obtained from these sites which cannot easily be obtained from cells within the central nervous system. As noted above, one of the earliest demonstrations of the electrical activity associated with synaptic activation was obtained here (Schaefer and Haass, 1939), and the identity of the transmitter substance involved at the junctions, acetylcholine, is more certainly established for these than for any other synapses.

Shortly after the introduction of microelectrode techniques, Fatt and Katz (1950, 1951) applied them to studies of neuromuscular transmission. Stimulation of the motor nerve during microelectrode recording from the muscle fiber in the region of an end-plate revealed that a potential was developed

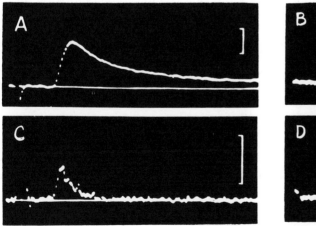
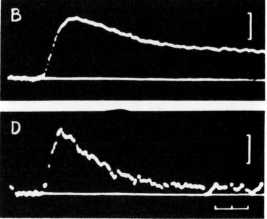

Figure 5.1. A, A typical end-plate potential, and *C*, the current generating it, from the sartorius muscle of a frog. *B* and *D*, The same after the addition of eserine to the bath. Time marker, 2 msec.; voltage calibrations, 2 mV; current calibrations, 1 x 10⁻⁷ amp. (From Takeuchi and Takeuchi, 1959, by permission of the Journal of Neurophysiology.)

whose amplitude was raised by increasing the strength of the applied stimulus; and, if large enough, the muscle fiber would respond by the production of an action potential. This graded "end-plate potential" (EPP) is thus in every respect the analogue of the EPSP evoked in a motoneurone. A typical EPP is shown in Figure 5.1A, recorded from a frog's sartorius muscle at 17° C. The peak of the EPP is high and comparatively early if a recording is made from the end-plate region itself. If recorded from points farther away along the muscle fiber, considerable distortion occurs as the potential is electrotonically propagated from its locus of origin.

Experiments to determine the equilibrium potential for the EPP and the time course of its generating current are more easily accomplished than was the case for motoneuronal synaptic potentials, both in that direct visual control of the penetration of the microelectrode is possible, and because pharmacological agents can be used to alter the activity of the end-plate region. Fatt and Katz (1951) and Takeuchi and Takeuchi (1959) have both estimated the equilibrium potential for the process at about –15 mV in amphibian junctions. The latter authors, who used a "voltage clamp" procedure directly to observe the end-plate current (Figure 5.1B), showed that it rose to a peak in about 0.8 msec. and thereafter decayed with a half time of 1.1 msec., the total duration of the current flow being 4 to 5 msec. Takeuchi and Takeuchi (1960) have also investigated the nature of the ions contributing to the end-plate potential. It should be noted that E_{EPP} lies on the negative side of zero membrane potential, and that therefore a complete membrane short-circuit, as was postulated for activated excitatory synapses at motoneurones, cannot explain the events which occur. Takeuchi and Takeuchi have been able to show, by alterations in the environmental ionic concentrations of a muscle *in vitro*, that both sodium and potassium ions move down their concentration gradients but that chloride ions do not; and they concluded that "as a first approximation, the transmitter makes the end-plate more permeable to sodium and potassium but not to chloride." There is a suggestion that, in some circumstances at least, an enhanced permeability to calcium may also occur. The relative contribution of sodium and potassium to the EPP was roughly equal, the ratio of the conductance changes $\dfrac{\Delta G_{Na}}{\Delta G_K}$ being 1.29. We

have seen that the distinction between the various ionic species in the generation of the IPSP was on the basis of their size, but this clearly cannot be the distinguishing feature here, since chloride ions are considerably smaller than sodium. Possibly, at neuromuscular junctions any pores opened in the activated subsynaptic membrane are charged in such a way as to prevent the passage of anions through them.

The time course of decay of the EPP has a time constant very similar to that of the muscle fiber membrane both in amphibian and mammalian muscle (Fatt and Katz, 1951; Boyd and Martin, 1956b). There is thus no indication that the transmitter action is prolonged beyond an initial brief (2 msec.) period, a suggestion borne out also by the direct observation of the postsynaptic current, which falls rapidly to zero from its peak (Figure 5.1B). The duration of transmitter action, and hence of the EPP, can of course be greatly prolonged by an anticholinesterase which will preserve the acetylcholine liberated into the synaptic gutter (Figure 5.1C,D). In mammalian muscle the end-plate potential has a generally similar character to that observed in amphibia, but with a shorter overall time course. The threshold depolarization required in mammalian muscle for initiation of an action potential in the fiber is 10 to 20 mV (Boyd and Martin, 1956b).

The localization of cholinesterase to the region of the subsynaptic membrane of the muscle is well known, and was first shown by an histochemical method by Koelle and Friedenwald (1949). The enzyme is located only in the region of the end-plate (Figure 5.2A) and closely follows the outlines of the synaptic gutter (Figure 5.2B), although there is evidence (the possible significance of which has been discussed on p. 22), that the highest concentrations of enzyme are not actually within the synaptic gutters. This excellent correlation between morphological findings and expectation based upon physiological grounds extends to all skeletal muscle junctions in vertebrates which have been examined.

There are striking changes which occur in the reactivity of a muscle after it has been deprived for a time of its normal innervation. It is well known that under these conditions many tissues become hypersensitive to the transmitter agent which is normally released upon the subsynaptic regions, and this effect is particularly striking in the case of skeletal muscle. Thus, for example, denervated mam-

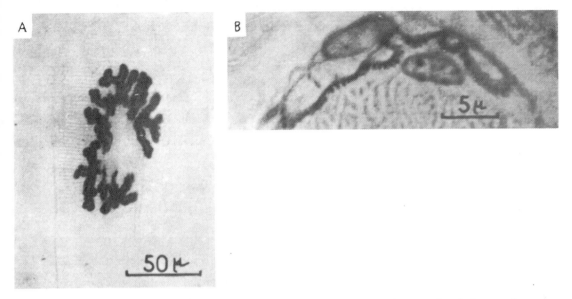

Figure 5.2. A, A lizard neuromuscular junction upon skeletal muscle, stained with the acetyl-thiocholine method for cholinesterase. B, Cross-section through a hedgehog neuromuscular junction stained to reveal cholinesterase and showing the synaptic gutters with lamellae. The nuclei have been counterstained with hemalum. (From Couteaux, 1958, by permission of Academic Press, Inc.)

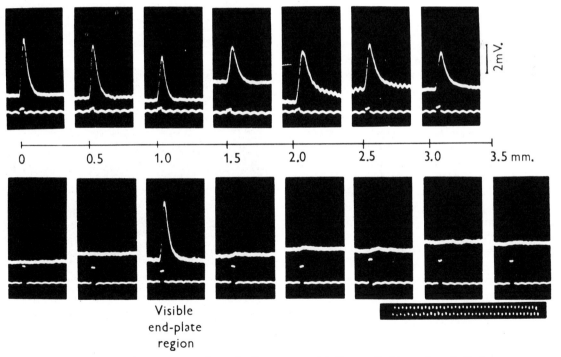

Figure 5.3. The sensitivity of muscle fibers to acetylcholine applied iontophoretically from a micropipette and recorded with an intracellular electrode. In a normal fiber (lower records), only application at a visible neuromuscular junction produced an end-plate potential; whereas in a muscle denervated 14 days previously, application anywhere on the muscle membrane produced a response of roughly equivalent amplitude and duration. Time marker, 100 c/sec. (From Axelsson and Thesleff, 1959, by permission of the Journal of Physiology.)

malian muscle may be 1000 times more sensitive than normal to acetylcholine administered intra-arterially (Brown, 1937). This reaction has been studied with the aid of micro methods by Axelsson and Thesleff (1959). They have applied acetylcholine iontophoretically from a microelectrode, and observed that whereas in the normal muscle only at the region of an end-plate was an application effective in producing a depolarization of the membrane, after 7 to 14 days denervation the whole of the muscle membrane became sensitive (Figure 5.3). They were further able to show that the whole of the membrane had acquired the characteristics formerly confined to the end-plate, i.e., it responded to applied acetylcholine by a current flow which had an equilibrium potential of –10 to –20 mV, and that current was carried in the main by sodium and potassium ions. It is of some interest to note in relation to the claim of Grundfest that chemically sensitive membranes are not electrically excitable (see p. 38), that the denervated muscle membrane retained is electrical excitability unaltered in spite of having developed a pronounced chemical sensitivity. The continued electrical excitability of denervated muscle membranes has, however, been disputed by Grundfest (1961). Axelsson and Thesleff have reported that the acetylcholine response of denervated membrane was not potentiated by anticholinesterase drugs and suggested that the membrane was devoid of this enzyme. This suggestion has not been borne out by the histochemical investigations of Casselman (1961), who has found that after denervation the cholinesterase normally found only at the end-plate becomes widely dispersed over the whole muscle fiber surface. It is tempting to correlate this finding with the observed development of acetylcholine sensitivity and to speculate upon the relationship of the enzyme to the structural matrix of the subsynaptic areas which respond to the transmitter by specific changes in their permeability characteristics.

The occurrence at neuromuscular junctions of spontaneous activity of low amplitude was first described by Fatt and Katz (1950) and has since been intensively investigated in frog muscle by Fatt and Katz (1952) and del Castillo and Katz (1954), and in mammalian muscle by Boyd and Martin (1956a) and Liley (1956a). Fatt and Katz (1952) thus describe their original observations: "While recording from the surface of isolated muscle fibres, we occasionally noticed a spontaneous discharge of small monophasic action potentials. The potentials varied somewhat in size, but had a very consistent time course, rising rapidly in 1 to 2 msec. and declining more slowly to one-half in about 3 to 4 msec. They were localized at one region of the fibre and their shape and spatial spread resembled the end-plate potential; moreover the discharge disappeared when a moderate dose of curarine was applied to the muscle." The small potentials which were so described were thus remarkably uniform, and in all respects save their size resembled the EPP. They could be

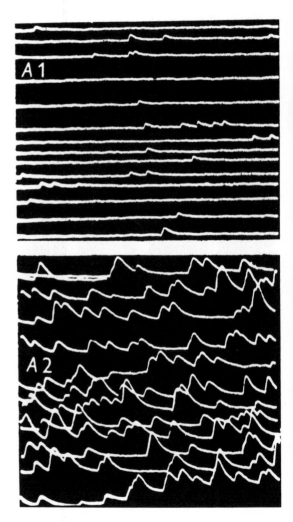

Figure 5.4. Spontaneous miniature end-plate potentials from the m. extensor longus dig. IV of the frog, (*A1*) before and (*A2*) after the addition of prostigmine to the bath. The effect is not an increase in frequency but only of amplitude and duration of the individual potentials. Duration of sweep, 300 msec. (From Fatt and Katz, 1952, by permission of the Journal of Physiology.)

localized to the end-plate region and were sensitive to those substances which normally affected the transmission process, e.g., curare and anticholinesterase drugs like prostigmine. Examples of the normal spontaneous discharge and its potentiation by prostigmine are shown in Figure 5.4. Fatt and Katz noted that the increase in amplitude and duration of the potentials caused by prostigmine was qualitatively similar to its effect upon the end-plate potential. It is reasonable to assume, then, that the small potentials are due to the action of acetylcholine upon the subsynaptic membrane.

The distribution of these miniature EPP's is completely random in time, and their essentially constant amplitude led to the hypothesis that they represent the spontaneous liberation of quantal units of the normal transmitter substance, acetylcholine (Fatt and Katt, 1952; del Castillo and Katz, 1954); and further that the EPP evoked by motor nerve stimulation is, in effect, the sum of a discrete number of such quantal units. Essentially analogous observations have been made by Liley (1956a) in the rat diaphragm, although there was some indication that at very short time intervals there could be interaction of the miniature potentials and their randomness thereby distorted. The effect of an impulse in the presynaptic axon is to increase enormously the statistical probability for the liberation of a quantum of acetylcholine, the factor being 100,000 times or more (Katz, 1958). Liley (1956b) has shown that the depolarization of the presynaptic endings increases the output of acetylcholine by 10-fold for each 15 mV, i.e., an action potential of 75 mV amplitude arriving at the junction would increase the output of acetylcholine by 100,000 times. It is not certain how this transformation of electrical into chemical potential is accomplished; however it has been suggested that calcium ions are in some intimate way involved (Hubbard, 1961) (see also p. 20).

It is tempting to equate the quantal unit of acetylcholine with some morphologically identifiable structure, and the synaptic vesicles found in all typical synapses, if that in fact is what the profiles seen represent, are the most obvious choice. While there is no direct evidence that the vesicles at the neuromuscular junction do contain acetylcholine, there is some evidence showing that certain vesicles of the central nervous system do (Whittaker, 1959; de Robertis, Pellegrino de Iraldi, Rodriguez de Lores Arnaiz, and Sal-

ganicoff, 1962). Furthermore, the concentration of the vesicles close to the prejunctional membrane is suggestive; Eccles (1961b) points out that if they were filled with an 0.15 M solution of acetylcholine, each would contain about 3000 molecules of the transmitter, and this is in good agreement with the amount calculated to be liberated for each quantum of activity, i.e., the amount required for the production of a unit miniature end-plate potential (del Castillo and Katz, 1954; Katz, 1958).

Inasmuch as there is evidence that all postsynaptic potentials are generated in much the same manner, it is of some interest to inquire whether miniature potentials have been located at other synaptic junctions, thus indicating the "leakage" of transmitter at these regions also. They are apparently present at other neuromuscular junctions (Takeuchi, 1959; Ginsborg, 1960; Dudel and Kuffler, 1961a; Burnstock and Holman, 1961, 1962a), but at central nervous synapses it is often not easy to distinguish between spontaneous miniature potentials and depolarizations caused by impulses arriving at synapses upon the cell. However, Katz and Miledi (1962) have reported the occurrence of such spontaneous miniature potentials in frog motoneurones, while Kolmodin and Skoglund (1958) had evidence for the quantal liberation of transmitter upon moto- and interneurones of mammalian spinal cord. Nishi and Koketsu (1960) and Blackman, Ginsborg, and Ray (1962) reported the presence of miniature postsynaptic potentials in amphibian sympathetic ganglion cells under conditions in which activation of the synapses could be excluded, and the potential units of which these postsynaptic potentials were built up were of the order of 1 mV in amplitude. However, this has been reported not to be true for mammalian sympathetic ganglia (Eccles, 1955), although Emmelin (1960) has obtained direct evidence for the appearance of acetylcholine from postganglionic parasympathetic endings in the absence of neuronal excitation. Since the spontaneous miniature potentials are presumably of no functional value, it is conceivable that the majority of interneuronal synapses do not show the same wastage as appears to occur at some peripheral junctions; but the increasing number of situations in which clear evidence of their occurrence has been obtained would, on the other hand, perhaps indicate the general nature of the phenomenon.

TRANSMISSION TO VERTEBRATE SMOOTH MUSCLE

Although a number of workers have investigated the electrical activity of smooth muscles from various sources with the aid of intracellular microelectrodes, the clearest analysis of the processes involved has been that of Burnstock and Holman (1961), who studied a muscle which does not show a spontaneous activity (the vas deferens), but which can be excited by stimulation of the hypogastric nerve.

The general character of the transmission processes described above for striated muscle has been found also for this smooth muscle. Thus, subliminal stimulation of the motor nerve gave rise to a slow depolarization of the cell, which Burnstock and Holman named the "junctional potential." This potential varied in size with the number of nerve fibers excited; however the time course was always approximately the same. It is clear, therefore,

that the slow potential change represents activity of the same type as that described for other transmission processes. If sufficiently large, such that the muscle cell was depolarized by about 40 mV, an action potential was evoked. The summation of subthreshold junctional potentials, giving rise ultimately to the production of an action potential, is shown in Figure 5.5.

In two obvious respects, however, the features of this transmission process are different. One is in the very prolonged time course of the whole process (note the time scale in Figure 5.5); thus, for example, the time for half decay of a junctional potential is about 150 msec. Since there is no reason to believe that the electrical properties of the smooth muscle cells are enormously different from those of other excitable tissues, it follows that the decay of the junctional potential is not passively determined by the time constant of the muscle membrane, but rather that the duration of transmitter action is greatly prolonged. Since the fibers innervating the vas deferens from the hypogastric nerves are postganglionic, the transmitter substance involved is presumably noradrenaline, and the extremely slow destruction of this substance when liberated has been demonstrated in other situations (Brown, Davies, and Gillespie, 1958). It would appear that this slow destruction, and therefore a prolonged action of the transmitter can adequately account for the slow decay of the junctional potential.

The second unusual feature is the variability of the latency between stimulation and onset of the postsynaptic potential change in different cells, differences up to 40 msec. having been recorded. Burnstock and Holman suggest that the differences may be related to the manner of application of the transmitter to the postjunctional structure, being in some instances diffusely applied rather than receiving it from discrete nerve endings. The uncertainty associated with the innervation pattern of smooth muscle (see p. 10) should be recalled in this connection.

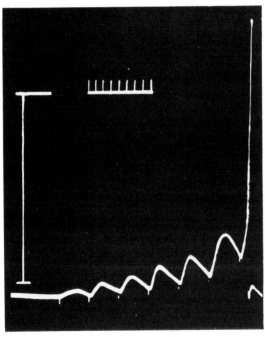

Figure 5.5. Intracellular record of the membrane potential of a cell of the vas deferens during repetitive submaximal stimulation of the hypogastric nerve. The first stimulus gave rise to a slow depolarization of about 5 mV, which had largely decayed by the time of the second stimulus; succeeding responses had a larger amplitude and greater rate of rise. Summation occurred until the membrane potential had fallen to –35 mV, when an action potential was initiated. Voltage calibration, 50 mV; the horizontal trace = 0 mV; time marker, 100 msec. (From Burnstock and Holman, 1961, by permission of the Journal of Physiology.)

VERTEBRATE HEART

The electrical effects upon the frog heart associated with stimulation of the vagus nerve have been studied by Hutter and Trautwein (1956) and by del Castillo and Katz (1957). In the sinus venosus during diastole, a slow

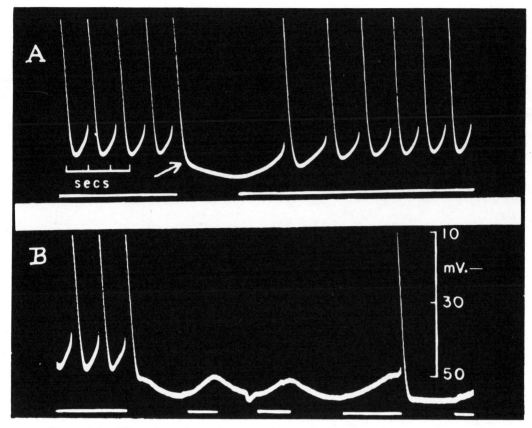

Figure 5.6. Effect of vagal stimulation on the membrane potential of a fiber of the sinus venosus of the frog heart. In *A*, the vagus was stimulated at 20/sec., indicated by the break in the reference line. The repolarization phase of the action potential is accelerated and reaches (arrow) a higher level of membrane potential than in previous cycles. This is followed by a slowly increasing polarization during the period of stimulation. In *B*, intermittent stimulation at 20/sec.; note the escaped beat at the start of the fourth stimulation period. (From Hutter and Trautwein, 1956, by permission of the Rockefeller Institute.)

depolarization (the pacemaker potential) develops, which initiates an action potential upon reaching an amplitude of 13 to 15 mV. If the vagi are stimulated, repolarization following the action potential is speeded and is continued until the membrane potential is at a more negative point than that reached in a previous cycle (Figure 5.6). The next beat is delayed because the rate of rise of the pacemaker potential has been reduced or it is completely abolished if the pacemaker potential fails to reach the threshold level. The transmitter substance released, acetylcholine, is thus acting in the same way as the inhibitory transmitter at motoneurones, i.e., by a relative hyperpolarization of the excitable membrane. This electrical sign of inhibition had been recognized by Gaskell (1887).

In conformity also with events at motoneurones, it would be expected that the hyperpolarization was due to an enhanced efflux of potassium ions or to an increased inward movement of chloride. Harris and Hutter (1956) and Hutter (1961) have described experiments in which the former effect has been directly demonstrated using radioactive tracers, both for the inhibitions produced by vagal stimulation and by the addition of acetylcholine to the bathing fluid, thus confirming the early experiments of Howell and Duke (1908), who showed that during vagal arrest there was a liberation of potassium from the heart. By contrast, no alteration in chloride conductance could be discerned, and it must therefore be concluded that the action of inhibitory synapses here is specifically to cause an increased potassium conductance through the membrane.

In an atropinized heart, stimulation of the vago-sympathetic trunk results in an increased frequency of the beat due to an increased rate of rise of the pacemaker potential, and at

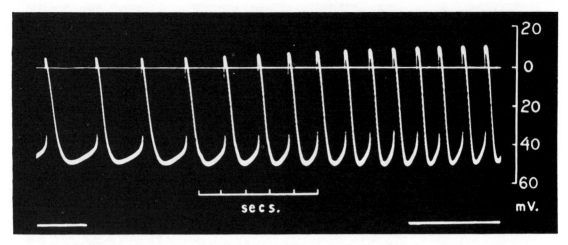

Figure 5.7. Effect of vagosympathetic stimulation on the membrane potential of a sinus venosus fiber in an atropinized heart. Stimulation at 20/sec. at the break in the reference line. The rate of rise of the slow depolarization is increased, leading to a greater frequency in production of action potentials; the overshoot of each action potential is also raised. (From Hutter and Trautwein, 1956, by permission of the Rockefeller Institute.)

the same time the "overshoot" of the action potential is also raised (Figure 5.7). Although the point has not been directly tested, this effect could be due to an enhanced sodium permeability due to the action of the transmitter, which would permit both a faster rate of rise of the pacemaker potential (which is, in all probability, due to a slowly increasing sodium penetration [Draper and Weidmann, 1951]) and would allow the peak of the action potential to approach more nearly to E_{Na}. Alternatively, a reduced permeability to potassium such as occurs in mammalian muscle under the influence of adrenaline (Goffart and Perry, 1951), might explain the effect.

GIANT SYNAPSE OF THE SQUID STELLATE GANGLION

Studies of this structure, whose morphological character has been described above, are of fundamental interest inasmuch as in this preparation the possibility exists for recording with intracellular electrodes both from the pre- and postjunctional sides of the synapse simultaneously. The results to be described have been obtained by Bullock and Hagiwara (1957) and Hagiwara and Tasaki (1958).

Several important hypotheses upon the mode of action of synapses which have been implicitly accepted in the above discussions have been directly confirmed with this preparation. Thus, most importantly, it has been possible to show that there is no direct spread of current from one side to the other of the synapse, for strong depolarizing or hyperpolarizing currents applied across either the pre- or postsynaptic fiber membranes are not detectable on the opposite side. Figure 5.8 shows the results obtained for a hyperpolarizing current. In *A*, a stimulus was delivered to the presynaptic axon, and the spike is seen there and after the synaptic delay in the postsynaptic structure. In *B*, a hyperpolarizing pulse was applied to the presynaptic fiber and in *C* to the postsynaptic, without there being in either case an effect upon the opposite side. A direct demonstration of the synaptic delay is also of interest, as is the fact that the delay is much prolonged by a lower temperature (1 to 2 msec. at 9° C, compared with about 0.5 msec. at 20°). A direct electrical demonstration of the existence of the cleft between pre- and postsynaptic membranes has also been possible.

Other features of the excitatory transmission process which have now become familiar have been detected also in this tissue. Thus, the postsynaptic potential, from which an action potential arises, is due to the breakdown in the normal permeability of the subsynaptic membrane, such that the transmembrane potential tends to be brought toward zero. Since at this synapse there is a single contact of the pre- and postsynaptic elements, there can be no question of summation of action, and under normal circumstances each presynaptic impulse generates a postsynaptic

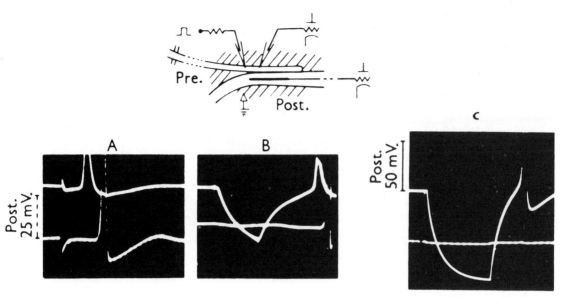

Figure 5.8. *A*, Simultaneous recording of the action potentials in the pre- (upper trace) and postsynaptic (lower trace) fibers of the giant synapse of the stellate ganglion of the squid *Loligo pealii*. The diagram above shows the arrangement of the electrodes. *B*, The effect of hyperpolarization of the presynaptic fiber (upper trace) and *C*, of the postsynaptic fiber (upper trace). In neither case is the membrane potential of the other half of the synapse affected. Duration of sweeps: 10 msec. (From Hagiwara and Tasaki, 1958, by permission of the Journal of Physiology.)

action potential. Only if the synapse is fatigued by repetitive stimulation does the full postsynaptic potential appear uncomplicated by a spike. The size of the postsynaptic potential can be markedly altered by the amplitude of the presynaptic spike, a 30 per cent reduction in its size almost completely preventing the liberation of transmitter from the presynaptic ending (see Figure 3.2). There is every reason to believe that in spite of its unusual morphology this giant synapse does not differ in any fundamental way from others that we have considered, and in this respect it is to be contrasted with the crayfish giant synapse, which will be discussed on p. 63.

STRETCH RECEPTOR NEURONES OF CRAYFISH

The anatomy of the sensory neurones lying in the thoracic and abdominal segments of crustacea was described originally for lobsters by Alexandrowicz (1951, 1952) and for crayfish by Florey and Florey (1955). Each segment possesses a pair of stretch receptor organs, and each organ consists of a pair of muscle fibers, each of which is interpenetrated by the dendrites of a separate sensory neurone. The innervation of these neurones

is not fully understood, but they both receive the synaptic endings of one fiber, among others, whose action is to inhibit the cell.

The generation of impulses in these neurones has been studied by Eyzaguirre and Kuffler (1955a,b); Florey (1955); and Edwards and Ottoson (1958). Stretch applied to the muscle fibers elicits repetitive discharge of the cells after a certain threshold has been attained, which in the case of one cell is quickly compensated, while in the other a sustained discharge continues with little or no adaptation during the period of stretch. A stretch which is subthreshold for the production of sensory action potentials in the axon nevertheless produces a depolarization of the neuronal membrane during the period of its application. The process of impulse generation is thus comparable to those that we have discussed, although in this case the required level of membrane potential change is produced not by the action of a transmitter but by the mechanical deformation of the dendrites which invest the muscle fibrils (Florey, 1955). The current flow to the dendritic region results in the threshold being attained for the production of an action potential in the first instance in the axon, from whence an antidromic impulse invades the rest of the cell soma (Edwards and Ottoson, 1958).

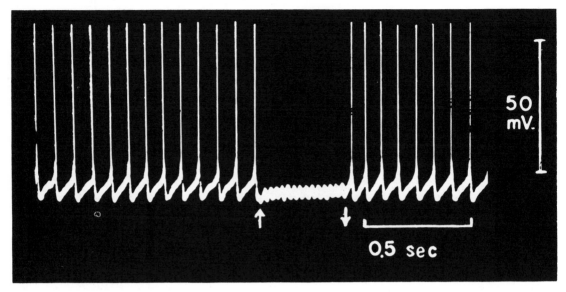

Figure 5.9. Intracellular record from the slowly adapting stretch receptor neurone of the crayfish. Stimulation of the inhibitory nerve supply (between the arrows) at a frequency of 34/sec. causes inhibition of the discharge of the cell by holding the membrane potential close to the most polarized point of previous cycles. The small deflections during inhibitory stimulation are IPSP's. (From Kuffler and Eyzaguirre, 1955, by permission of the Rockefeller Institute.)

Stimulation of the inhibitory axon innervating the stretch receptor neurones during their repetitive activation by stretch will interrupt the generation of impulses (Kuffler and Eyzaguirre, 1955) (Figure 5.9). The effect is produced by a typical synaptic mechanism, in which a graded postsynaptic potential is produced in the sensory neurone. This potential differs from others that have been described above only in that its equilibrium potential is close to or even at a slightly greater level of depolarization than the normal resting potential of the cell, so that in many cases it is manifested by a depolarizing rather than an hyperpolarizing response. Nevertheless, it has as a basis an ionic mechanism similar to those other postsynaptic inhibitory processes that have been described, in that an increase in chloride and/or potassium permeability is responsible for the current flow. It is important to note that the development of a hyperpolarizing potential is therefore not obligatory for the existence of an IPSP. It is also worth mentioning that this is an example of the autonomy of the various processes impinging on a cell; thus, for example, as we have seen, an IPSP can be converted to a depolarizing response even in a mammalian motoneurone by suitably changing the resting potential of the cell, and if this depolarizing reaction is large enough, an action potential may be evoked within that cell. In such a

manner, an "inhibitory" stimulus may result in the excitation of the postsynaptic cell, although it should be noted that such a situation presumably never arises physiologically. The important point is that inhibition does not involve any interference with the impulse-generating mechanism, nor need it, as in the stretch receptors, result in the hyperpolarization of the cell membrane.

NEURONES OF THE CEREBRAL CORTEX

The firing pattern of single cells of the mammalian cerebral cortex and the effects thereon of stimulations applied to other parts of the nervous system have been investigated by a great many workers. Such studies are of great interest and fundamental importance, but do not fall within the scope of this chapter. Intracellular records have been obtained by some investigators, however; thus Phillips (1956, 1959) has studied the reaction of the Betz cells of the motor cortex, while Creutzfeldt, Baumgartner and Schon (1956): Li, Cullen, and Jasper (1956); Buser and Albe-Fessard (1957); and Li (1959) have successfully penetrated neurones of the postcentral gyrus; and Li, Ortiz-Galvin, Chou, and Howard (1960) those of the striate cortex. Neurones of sensory areas could be made to respond to appropriate afferent stimulation.

The Betz cells respond to antidromic volleys in the medullary pyramids by the generation of action potentials which show both an initial segment and a somadendritic component similar to those noted above for motoneurones. Subthreshold antidromic stimulation yielded a slow depolarization of the cell membrane without antidromic invasion, which appeared to be due to the recurrent collaterals with which these cells are prominently provided (Cajal, 1955). These slow potentials are thus EPSP's and Phillips (1959) showed that if they were large enough, an orthodromic action potential was set up in the cell. Weak antidromic stimulation was also able to cause hyperpolarization and inhibition of the Betz cells, again by a mechanism involving axon collaterals, in this instance presumably analogous to Renshaw cell activation in the spinal cord. Rather similar results have been obtained by Sawa, Maruyama, Kaji, and Hanai (1960). Phillips discussed in some detail the purpose of such a mechanism, pointing out that in the motor area of the cortex, in contrast to the cord, high frequencies of firing are required, and that an inhibitory process especially effective at higher frequencies of stimulation was somewhat unexpected. A damping action of this type would, however, act to prevent the spread of electrical activity such as is manifest in epileptic cortex, and this might represent the "intrinsic mechanism of some cortical neurones" (Li, Chou, and Howard, 1961) whose disturbance could lead to an epileptic attack. It may be noted parenthetically, that a recurrent inhibitory mechanism similar to that described here and at motoneurones may be widespread in the nervous system. Thus, for example, very similar mechanisms have been described as occurring in hippocampal neurones (Kandel, Spencer, and Brinley, 1961) and in the cerebellum (Granit and Phillips, 1956).

Orthodromic stimulation of afferent pathways can lead both to excitation and to inhibition of neurones of the somato-sensory cortex (Creutzfeldt, Baumgartner, and Schon, 1956) or of the visual cortex (Li, Ortiz-Galvin, Chou, and Howard, 1960) through the production of postsynaptic potentials which owe their inception to mechanisms presumably identical to those which have been discussed in detail in Chapter 4. There are, however, two additional characteristics of cortical cells

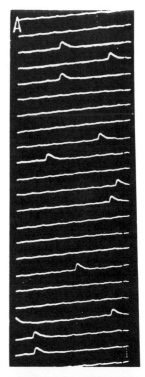

Figure 5.10. A, Spontaneous, small intracellular potentials from a neurone of the cerebral cortex of the cat. The strips of record are continuous from above. Voltage calibration, 2 mV; time calibration, 5 msec. (From Li, 1959, by permission of the Journal of Neurophysiology.) B, Rhythmic oscillatory potentials, some giving rise to action potentials, recorded above at high gain, and lower gain (voltage calibration, 50 mV) below. Time marker, 5 msec. (From Li, Chou, and Howard, 1961, by permission of Elsevier Publishing Company.)

which have been noted both by Li and by Phillips. Spontaneous action potentials which could not be correlated either with damage or stimulation were frequently noted, associated with slow membrane depolarizations up to the firing level for the neurone. Such spontaneous discharges could be continuous or could come in bursts, and their appearance is due to pacemakers within the cells themselves (Fessard, 1956). Secondly, the resting potential of cortical cells is markedly unstable (Li, Chou, and Howard, 1961), showing oscillatory depolarizations which may not reach the firing level (Figure 5.10*B*) or which may be more random in character, resembling in this latter case the miniature end-plate potentials seen at neuromuscular junctions (Figure 5.10*A*) (Li, 1959). The oscillatory type were found most frequently in the presence of a considerable degree of background depolarization.

OTHER NEURONES OF THE CENTRAL NERVOUS SYSTEM

It will by now be accepted as a reasonable proposition that the mechanisms described for motoneurones have a wide applicability, both in the mammalian central nervous system and in other very diverse situations. It is, therefore, not profitable to discuss the synaptic mechanisms which have been described for other neurones in detail, but merely to indicate that such have been studied and to mention briefly any differences from the typical pattern which may have been noticed to exist.

(1) Spinal Interneurones. (Eccles, Fatt, and Koketsu, 1954; Frank and Fuortes, 1956; Haapanen, Kolmodin, and Skoglund, 1958; Hunt and Kuno, 1959; Eccles and Lundberg, 1959). These cells, which mediate both excitatory and inhibitory reflex actions, characteristically show a multiple response to a single liminal synaptic excitation. Those cells which receive both Ia and Ib afferent innervation do not show an initial segment-somadendritic separation in their action potentials, while others receiving cutaneous afferent inflow have this characteristic clearly in evidence. The prolonged nature of the slow depolarization of the membrane to the firing level, which gives rise to a burst of action potentials, is presumably to be related to the long continued action of the excitatory transmitter released upon these neurones. (For a further consideration of this question, see p. 80).

(2) Cells of the Spinocerebellar Tracts. (Curtis, Eccles, and Lundberg, 1958; Eccles, Hubbard, and Oscarsson, 1961; Eccles, Oscarsson and Willis, 1961.) These cells show typical EPSP's and IPSP's in response to volleys in afferent fibers. Both dorsal and ventral groups show considerable convergence of excitatory input from various nerves, the effect being particularly noticeable in the ventral group. An example of a "double" EPSP, due

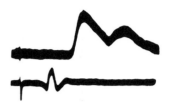

Figure 5.11. A "double" EPSP recorded from a neurone of the dorsal spinocerebellar tract, evoked by maximal stimuli in groups I and II afferent fibers. The record from the corresponding posterior root is shown below the intracellular record. (From Eccles, Oscarsson, and Willis, 1961, by permission of the Journal of Physiology.)

to the convergence of impulses from Group Ia and II fibers, upon a single dorsal spinocerebellar tract cell is given in Figure 5.11.

(3) Purkinje Cells of the Cerebellum. (Granit and Phillips, 1956.) These cells, in addition to the responses now familiar, show an unusual type of inhibitory reaction which has been named "inhibition by inactivation." The observation was that, both spontaneously and occasionally in response to stimulation of the fastigial nucleus, the natural discharge of a cell could be interrupted for periods of 15 to 30 msec. Intracellular recording during that time revealed that the falling phase of an action potential was greatly slowed during this "inactivation," and that during the period of inhibition the full level of repolarization was not attained. The inhibition was thus due to continued depolarization of the neuronal membrane, which was held at a level above its normal firing threshold.

The latency of the response can be as brief as 1.5 msec., and the presumption is, therefore, that a comparatively simple mechanism underlies it. Since fastigial nucleus stimulation was not invariably effective in its production, Granit and Phillips concluded that collaterals of the Purkinje axons were not involved. They suggested as the most likely source of the depolarization synaptic contacts arising from the basket cells and especially concentrated around the axon hillock of the Purkinje neurones. Powerful excitation of these synapses, leading to a depolarizing postsynaptic potential with a long time constant of decay, was therefore felt to be the most likely basis.

(4) Cells of the Dorsal Root Ganglia. (Sato and Austin, 1961.) The action potentials of these cells do not exhibit an initial segment-somadendritic break on the rising phase, nor is there any sign of a slow de-

polarization preceding the spike. They have no dendrites and receive no synaptic contacts; however the neurones are enclosed in a covering of capsular cells, and the suggestion has been made that these may so restrict the extracellular space that the soma is normally maintained in a slightly depolarized state, and, therefore, that the normally appearing slow potential change which precedes an action potential does not occur.

GIANT GANGLION CELLS OF
APLYSIA DEPILANS

The anatomy of these molluscan ganglia is not fully worked out, and studies of the giant neurones contained in them present a number of unusual features (Arvanitaki and Cardot, 1941; Bullock, 1961) which need not concern us here. The cells are pigmented and respond both by depolarizations and hyperpolarizations to light (Arvanitaki and Chalazonitis, 1960), and they are also sensitive to such chemical stimuli as changes in the CO_2 content of their environment (Chalazonitis and Sugaya, 1958; Chalazonitis, 1961) or to mechanical deformation (Chalazonitis and Arvanitaki, 1961).

The neurones respond to presynaptic stimulation by the development of postsynaptic potentials of both excitatory and inhibitory character (Tauc, 1958), whose interactions have been studied in some detail. These processes appear to be precisely analogous to others which have been described above; there are, however, two points worthy of note. One is the very prolonged nature of the synaptic action, which may have a time constant of decay (in the case of the EPSP) of 120 msec. (Table IV), while the time constant of decay of the IPSP is of the order of 50 msec. Inasmuch as there is excellent evidence for believing that the inhibitory transmitter substance may be acetylcholine (Tauc and Gerschenfeld, 1960, 1962), which usually has a very brief duration of action, the prolonged postsynaptic potentials would indicate the presence of highly restrictive barriers surrounding the activated synapses.

The second point of note is in regard to the site of origin of action potentials generated by the cells. Tauc (1960b) has shown that the action potentials in a giant nerve cell are initiated at some distance from the cell soma (up to 2 mm away) and are conducted anti-dromically to invade the soma itself. This pattern is similar to that described above for the stretch receptor neurones of crayfish. Furthermore, the usual synaptic transmission is maintained despite the excision of the cell body (Tauc, 1960a), thus lending physiological confirmation to the suggestion of Hanström (1925) that functional synaptic contact can exist at the level of the axon.

There is also evidence that these cells are subject to a presynaptic inhibition analogous to that discussed above for motoneurones (Tauc, 1960c), in which the amplitude of the EPSP is reduced without the appearance of a conductance change in the postsynaptic neurone as a consequence of the inhibitory stimulation. Although more detailed studies of the process have not been made, there is no reason to think that the underlying mechanism is different here from that taking place in the mammalian spinal cord.

Tauc (1959) has also some evidence to show that a type of ephaptic transmission occurs between contiguous cells. He has demonstrated that the appearance of an action potential in one cell can result in the generation of a slow potential having a superficial resemblance to an EPSP in a second cell, but without there being any measurable delay between the two processes. The potential change in the second cell is thus clearly initiated by electrotonic current flow from the first, but its maximum amplitude does not occur until long after the peak of the action potential in the first neurone (Figure 5.12), and therefore the potential is not simply a reflection of the impulse but indicates an active change in the membrane of the second cell. Further details of this process are lacking, but clearly this mechanism provides another means of excitation of the cell and is one which can act to sum with the more usual synaptic processes.

GANGLIONIC TRANSMISSION
IN CRAYFISH

The possible existence of ephaptic transmission processes in Aplysia has introduced the notion of the spread of excitation from one neurone to another without the intervention of the specialized mechanisms which are now associated with synapses. As a result of recent work it seems probable that similar processes, which do not involve the libera-

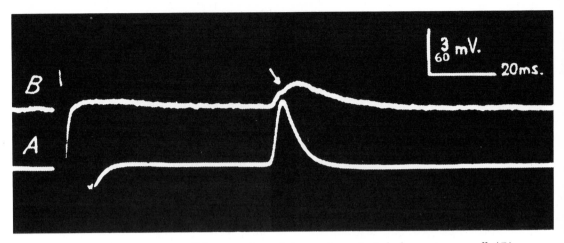

Figure 5.12. An intracellular recording of the passive potential change in one cell (*B*) brought about by stimulation of an adjacent cell whose response is shown by (*A*). Note that the peak of the passive change occurs only after the summit of the action potential (arrow) in *A*. (From Tauc, 1959, by permission of Gauthier-Villars.)

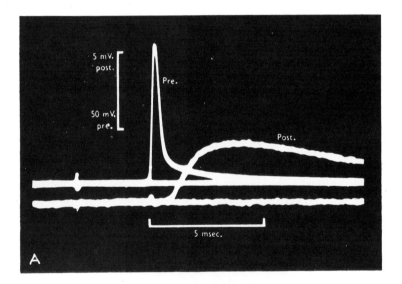

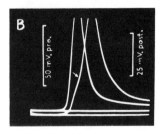

Figure 5.13. Responses of crayfish synapses. *A* shows the EPSP recorded from one of the smaller fibers of the third motor root (Post.) following stimulation of the lateral giant fiber. Compare the length of the synaptic delay in this case with that shown in *B* (arrow), which illustrates the postsynaptic response and the action potential in the giant motor fiber. Total duration of sweep in *B*, 4 msec. (From Furshpan and Potter, 1959, by permission of the Journal of Physiology.)

tion of a synaptic transmitter substance, occur also in other situations, one instance in particular having been studied in crayfish. In addition there are, as we have noted above, synapses in crustacea which do show the typical pattern of behavior; and neuromuscular transmission in these animals also has the familiar features, with the additional aspect that inhibition of both pre- and postsynaptic types can occur at these peripheral sites (Hoyle and Wiersma, 1958a,b; Dudel and Kuffler, 1961a,b,c). Detailed considerations of these mechanisms, which are analogous to those described above, does not seem to be necessary here.

This section will be concerned only with those processes which have certain anomalous features. The anatomy of the giant motor synapses has been described in Chapter 2, and the nature of the transmission process at this site has been studied in detail by Furshpan and Potter (1959). Here again, as in the squid synapse, both pre- and postsynaptic elements are large enough to be penetrated by microelectrodes. A typical record is shown in Figure 5.13B, in which the brevity of the synaptic delay should be compared with that of Figure 5.13A, recorded from another synapse in the same crayfish motor root.

The most striking feature of this transmission process is the brevity of the delay occurring at the synapse (compare Figure 5.13 with Figure 5.8, obtained in the squid giant synapse), which was estimated by Furshpan and Potter to be 0.12 msec. on the average. This time is so much smaller than those measured at other synapses that Furshpan and Potter concluded that in this situation an "electrical," as opposed to a "chemical," transmission mechanism was operative; i.e., that the spread

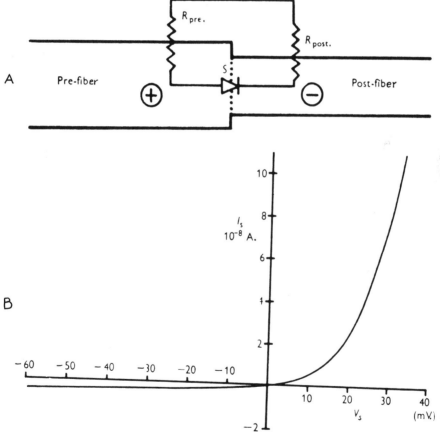

Figure 5.14. A, The equivalent circuit for the giant motor synapse of crayfish. $R_{pre.}$ and $R_{post.}$ are the "input resistances" of the two fibers and S, the synaptic resistance. The plus and minus signs indicate the direction of the potential difference across the junction for which S is small. For further details, see text. B, The current-voltage characteristics of the synapse. Positive values of V_s signify that the presynaptic fiber was electrically positive with respect to the postsynaptic. The synapse only transmits under this condition. (From Furshpan and Potter, 1959, by permission of the Journal of Physiology.)

of current from the presynaptic activation directly resulted in the development of the postsynaptic potential in the second fiber. Such a situation would require that the separation between the two elements should be as small as possible, unlike the required wide synaptic cleft at chemical synapses, and it will be recalled that Robertson (1955) had demonstrated the very close apposition of the pre- and postsynaptic fibers in these crayfish synapses.

In spite of this feature, however, the structure functions as a true synapse, in the sense that transmission across it can occur in only one direction. Thus, if depolarizing or hyperpolarizing currents were passed across the pre- and postsynaptic fibers, it was found that only depolarizations could cross orthodromically and hyperpolarizations antidromically. The conclusion was drawn that the junction behaves as a rectifier whose resistance would be low only when the inside of the presynaptic fiber became more positive, i.e., when it was depolarized. The equivalent electrical circuit is shown in Figure 5.14A, whose operation is thus described by Furshpan and Potter:

"R_{PRE} and R_{POST} represent the input resistances of the two fibres. The insides of the axons are separated by the synaptic resistance S which is shown as a rectifier. It is apparent that any change in potential across R_{PRE} would also alter the PD across R_{POST}, and vice versa, provided that S is not extremely large. To explain the results of the above experiments, S is assumed to be low only when the inside of the PRE fibre becomes more positive (depolarization), or when the POST fibre becomes more internally negative (hyperpolarization); that is, both situations give rise to a PD across the synapse of the same sign and the rectifier is assumed to have a low resistance for PD's of this direction."

Direct confirmation of the correctness of this hypothesis was made in experiments in which the current/voltage relationships of the two fibers were determined, and the complete current/voltage characteristics of the rectifier found in such experiments is shown in Figure 5.14B.

Among the many different varieties that have been investigated, these excitatory giant synapses in crayfish are so far unique in their mode of operation in that their action is not transmitted by the release of a chemical transmitter agent.* The functional significance of the arrangement is not understood, for with

*In a paper presented at the XXII International Physiological Congress, 1962, A. R. Martin and G. Pilar reported the existence of electrical transmission at synapses of the ciliary ganglion of the chick.

the single exception of the shorter delay, it confers no advantage over the usual mechanism. It is, of course, possible to consider that the typical chemical synapse represents a point of weakness and of sensitivity to poisons and to fatigue which would not be the case for these crustacean structures, but the preeminent importance of these giant motor synapses to the ecology of the organism, requiring that they should receive special protection, has not been established. Nevertheless, it is curious that the crayfish possesses these unusual synapses and in addition typical chemical ones. The close structural similarities of these giant junctions and those in the stellate ganglion of the squid, a point noted before, is worthy of mention again, for in spite of their strikingly similar appearance the two junctions are fundamentally distinct in their mode of operation.

The giant axons of the crayfish (and of some other animals) are segmented, and at the septa which divide the segments another purely electrical transmission process occurs. Impulses cross these junctions with very small delay (about 0.2 msec.) (Watanabe and Grundfest, 1961); but in contrast to the synapses discussed, transmission can occur in both directions. There is, therefore, no rectifying property to the septal membranes. The postjunctional membrane responds by the generation of a slow "septal potential" to prejunctional stimulation (Watanabe and Grundfest, 1961) (Figure 5.15), and some delay upon the transmission of information through the septa is thereby imposed. However, in agreement with Eccles (1961b), it would seem reasonable not to classify these septal regions as synaptic membranes.

SYNAPSES AT MAUTHNER CELLS

The structure of the synaptic endings impinging upon the paired Mauthner cells of the medulla of teleost fishes and their topographical distribution upon the giant cells have been dealt with above. There is no reason to suppose that the endings either of the typical bouton or of the club-like type are in any way unusual or differ in their actions from other ordinary synapses.

There occurs in these cells a collateral inhibition which has the typical character with which we are now familiar. The discharge of each cell can activate a postsynaptic inhibi-

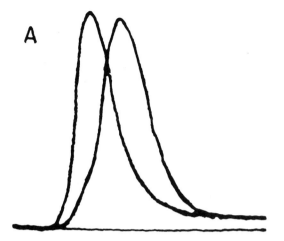 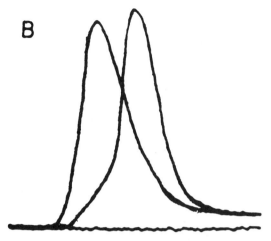

Figure 5.15. Septal transmission in the lateral giant fibers of the crayfish. Two recording electrodes, one on each side of the septum, were inserted 50 μ apart. In *A*, the stimulus was delivered to the rostral and in *B* to the caudal part of the nerve cord, indicating that transmission occurs in either direction across the septum. Note also the slowly developing "post-septal" potential in each case. Duration of sweeps: 2.5 msec. (From Watanabe and Grundfest, 1961, by permission of the Rockefeller Institute.)

tory process in itself, and to a much more marked extent in the contralateral member of the pair. This inhibition has a latency of two msec. following the discharge of the Mauthner cell, the resultant IPSP has an equilibrium potential near the level of the resting potential and for a duration of 10 to 20 msec. the neurone is effectively inhibited.

In addition to this process, there is a second which is so far unique. The inhibition follows an action potential in the cell by a delay of 1 to 1.5 msec., but has a duration of only one msec. It can block antidromic invasion of the cell and raise the threshold for orthodromic activation. It appears as an extracellular positivity of 10 to 15 mV amplitude which reaches its maximum near the axon hillock, and only a small fraction of this positivity can be recorded intracellularly. The external positivity hyperpolarizes the axon hillock of the cell, and thus prevents the passage of an impulse through this region. The hyperpolarization is a passive process, and no change occurs in the membrane conductance of the cell (T. Furukawa and E. J. Furshpan, Personal Communication).

Since the hyperpolarization is centered upon the hillock, one is compelled to consider that the current is derived from the spiral fibers which surround the region (see p. 6), and the latency of 1.5 msec. would indicate that one interneurone is presumably interposed between the discharging axon collaterals of the (predominantly contralateral) Mauthner

cell. Thus, one has another example of an electrical synapse, this time giving rise to inhibition rather than excitation of the postsynaptic structure. The more general significance of the observation stems from the fact that other cells are also known to possess similar structures around their axon hillocks (cf. Bodian, 1937), and the possible existence of such a mechanism in the mammalian spinal cord, in the light of Szentágothai's observations (1958), remains to be investigated.

SUMMARY

This chapter has drawn attention to the very remarkable similarity in qualitative detail which has been found at synaptic junctions in a wide variety of situations, at the same time pointing out the considerable quantitative variation, especially in the time of synaptic action, which can occur (see Table IV). From these observations it is possible to make certain statements about the main features of synaptic action, and to distinguish between "chemically" and "electrically" mediated synapses (cf. Furshpan and Potter, 1959; Eccles, 1961b).

(1) Features Common to All Synapses

(A) Transmission in one direction only.
Although this is true in the one case

because of the liberation of a transmitter agent only from the presynaptic endings and in the other case because of the rectifying properties of the system, the effect is the same.

(B) Postsynaptic potentials in the two types of synapse are very similar, since in both cases they are generated in the postsynaptic membrane by the flow of depolarizing or hyperpolarizing current.

(C) Hyperpolarization of the postsynaptic membrane brings about a larger EPSP, in the one case because of the ionic mechanism responsible for the EPSP's, and in the other because of the rectification.

(2) Properties Exclusive to Chemical Synapses

(A) Liberation of a specific chemical transmitter which acts upon the postsynaptic membrane so as to cause characteristic changes in the membrane permeability.

(B) A comparatively long synaptic delay attributable to the mobilization and to diffusion of the transmitter across the synaptic cleft.

(C) Presence of synaptic vesicles in the presynaptic element only.

(D) Pharmacological properties attributable to interference with the normal metabolism of the transmitter.

(3) Properties Exclusive to Electrical Synapses

(A) A very brief synaptic delay.

(B) A very narrow or negligible synaptic cleft.

In addition to these, there are several other matters which we have discussed whose wide applicability has not yet been demonstrated. Such, for example, are the miniature end-plate potentials observed at neuromuscular junctions, which would of course be observable only at chemical synapses. The question of the electrical inexcitability of the subsynaptic membrane itself has been discussed on p. 38; but there is evidence, as we have seen, that this is not necessarily a characteristic of synaptic membranes. It is interesting in this connection that Furshpan and Potter (1959) were able to show that the subsynaptic membrane of the electrical giant motor synapses were in fact electrically inexcitable, the subsynaptic area itself merely providing an efficient channel for the flow of current for the depolarization of the membranes adjacent to the synaptic region.

Chapter 6

TRANSMITTER SUBSTANCES AND THE PHARMACOLOGY OF SYNAPSES

In Chapter 3 the fundamental work which led to the suggestion of the function of acetylcholine as the mediator of parasympathetic postganglionic nervous action was described. This chapter considers the possible role of this and of other known chemical entities as transmitters at other synapses, and describes some of the information available regarding some synapses where the chemical agent involved has not been identified. Further, the action of compounds present in the brain and having effects upon neurones but which are not themselves synaptic transmitter substances will be briefly discussed.

Table V lists the distributions in various areas of the nervous system of the materials, both of known and unknown chemical constitution, which are of importance in this connection. It is evident that some regions are comparatively rich in almost all the agents under consideration, while others are largely deficient in them. It would seem a reasonable inference, therefore, that there remain to be detected other synaptic transmitters whose regions of highest concentration might be expected to be those which show only a low content of presently recognized substances.

ACETYLCHOLINE

The evidence leading to the concept that acetylcholine is liberated from the peripheral endings of the vagus nerve upon the heart and is there responsible for the transmission of the action of stimulation of the nerve was re-

viewed in Chapter 3. Some years later, experiments clearly demonstrating the release of acetylcholine at other synapses where the "nicotinic" effects of the substance had been recognized for some time, i.e. in sympathetic ganglia and at neuromuscular junctions, were performed, with the result that the transmitter action of acetylcholine in these peripheral situations is now largely unquestioned. The evidence resulting from those experiments is summarized in Table VI. Comparison of these findings with the list of criteria for establishing the likely identity of transmitter substances (see p. 23) shows that, while not complete in every detail, the evidence is sufficient to ascribe beyond reasonable doubt a transmitter role to acetylcholine. In the few instances in which the process can conveniently be studied, it would appear that parasympathetic ganglionic synapses are also cholinergically mediated (Emmelin and Muren, 1950; Perry and Talesnik, 1953). However, it must be pointed out that the identification of acetylcholine as the substance actually released is based upon biological tests and not upon the chemical identification of the material and, furthermore, that there are some differences in the actions of drugs upon the effects of injected acetylcholine, on the one hand, compared with those upon nerve stimulation on the other. This has been emphasized by Kewitz and Reinert (1954a,b) and by Kewitz (1954), who have in consequence questioned whether in fact acetylcholine is the transmitter of ganglionic synapses. Furthermore, E. A. Hosein (Personal Communi-

TABLE V. THE DISTRIBUTION OF CERTAIN COMPOUNDS AND

(Conspicuously high values in cellular areas

UNITS / REFERENCES / SPECIES	NORADRENALINE μg./gm. 8,9,14,21,33 — Dog	Cat	Human	DOPAMINE μg./gm. 8,9,14,33 — Dog	Cat	Human	5-HYDROXYTRYPTAMINE μg./gm. 8,11,12,29,32 — Dog	Cat	Human	DOPA DECARBOXYLASE % Caudate Nucleus 22 — Cat	MONOAMINE OXIDASE % Caudate Nucleus 10,11,31 — Dog	ACETYLCHOLINE μg./gm. 3,25 — Cat	Human	CHOLINE ACETYLASE % Caudate Nucleus 16,17, — Dog
Cerebral cortex	0.11						0.17	0.24		3	87½		0.7	
Frontal	0.13	0.22	0.02	0.07	0.08	0			0.04			4.5		24
Motor														56
Parietal	0.12	0.23	0.03	0.08	0.10	0				4		2.8		45
Occipital									0.06			2.2		45½
Caudate nucleus	0.10	0.22	0.04	5.90	8.00	3.12	0.72	1.60	0.27	100	100			100
Globus pallidus	0.08	0.20	0.05	1.63	1.90	0.32			0.08		87½	2.7	0.5	
Putamen			0.02			5.27			0.23		94			
Olfactory bulb	0.05	0.03					0.35		0.01	5½	61½	1.3		43
Hippocampus	0.14			0.13			0.64		0.11	6½				
Corpus callosum							0			9½		8.5		20½
Internal capsule			0			0.42	0	0.13			50	1.5		27½
Septal region			0.03			0.04	1.50	1.40	0.03	33½	130			
Crus cerebri			0				0						0.5	39½
Diencephalon (without hypothal.)	0.17	0.34		0.09	0.16									
Thalamus (whole)							0.57	1.10		32	105	3		79
Anterior nuclei		0.02			0.07									107½
Medial nuclei		0.09			0.03				0.24					92
Lateral nuclei		0.04			0.01				0.22					
Hypothalamus (whole)	0.76	2.05		0.26	0.75		1.70	2.00		59½	174	1.9		
Anterior nuclei		0.96						0.18	0.35	62½				
Intermediate nuc.		1.19						0.14	0.48	63				
Posterior nuclei		0.31						0.22	0.30	58				
Lateral geniculate	0.07						0	0		8	90		0.8	82½
Medial geniculate	0.13						0			10	10			47
Mesencephalon (whole)							1.00	1.70		51½	90	1.6		
Superior colliculi	0.16				0.12		0.13			16		1.7		82
Inferior colliculi	0.11				0.15		0.10			16				35
Central grey matter										41½				
Substantia nigra					0.04		0.40							40
Red nucleus					0.22		0.19			43				68½
Mes. reticular form.	0.35									64½				
Cerebellum (whole)	0.06	0.13		0.03	0.02		~0	0.27		1½	99½	0.2	0.1	
Cortex		0.02			0.02									6½
Dentate nuc.		0.01			0.08									16½
Pons	0.41	0.52	0.04	0.10	0.11	0	0.38	0.70	0.19	24	100	2.8	0.2	
Medulla (whole)	0.37	0.39		0.13			0.63	1.20		17½	119	1.5	0.16	
Pyramids	0.06						0					0.2		10
IV Ventricle	0.27				0.13		0.30		0.50					
Nuc. cun. & grac.	0.11													68
Area postrema	1.04						0.26							
Spinal cord (whole)							0					6.4	0.45	
Ant. horn	0.18											1.5		120
Ant. roots	0.06						0					15.0		186
Post. horn	0.12											2.5		81
Post. roots	0.01						0					~0		
Stellate ganglion	4.67						0					44.0		
Sup. cervical ganglion	6.81						0					30.3		
Optic tract							0			2½	75			27½
Optic nerve												0.3		4½
Vagus nerve							0.03					8.0		

References

1. Amin, Crawford and Gaddum (1954).
2. Ashby, Garzoli and Schuster (1952).
3. Barsoum (1935).
4. Baxter and Roberts (1959).
5. Baxter and Roberts (1960).
6. Baxter and Roberts (1961).
7. Berl and Waelsch (1958).
8. Bertler (1961).
9. Bertler and Rosengren (1959).
10. Birkhäuser (1940).
11. Bogdanski, Weissbach and Udenfriend (1956).
12. Bogdanski, Weissbach and Udenfriend (1958).
13. Burgen and Chipman (1951).
14. Carlsson (1959).
15. Crossland (1960).
16. Feldberg, Harris and Lin (1951).
17. Feldberg and Vogt (1948).
18. Florey and Florey (1958).

ENZYME SYSTEMS IN SOME AREAS OF THE NERVOUS SYSTEM

of the central nervous system are underlined.)

CHOLINES-TERASE % Caudate Nucleus 2,13,26,27,28 Dog	Human	HISTAMINE µg./gm. 19,23,34,35 Dog	Cat	SUBSTANCE P Units/gm. 1, 29, 30, 36 Dog	Human	VASO-DILATOR MATERIAL % Caudate Nucleus 20 Horse	FACTOR I Units/gm. 18 Beef	GLUTAMIC ACID µg./gm. 7 Rat	γ-AMINO-BUTYRIC ACID µg./gm. 4, 5, 6, 7 Rat	GLUTAMIC ACID DECAR-BOXYLASE % Caudate Nucleus 24 Monkey	CEREBELLAR EXCITATORY FACTOR % Thalamus 15 Dog	UNITS REFERENCES SPECIES
5	3	0.13	~0.1			3	75	170	260			Cerebral cortex
10				23	43		126			82		Frontal Motor
7½				19			177					Parietal
				20	39		122			113½		Occipital
				14								
00	100	~0.1	~0.4	90	85	100	235		310	100		Caudate nucleus
50	27				112		296			206		Globus pallidus
	122				64		169			101½		Putamen
6½				6				144	440			Olfactory bulb
				15								Hippocampus
2	1½			8	2		30	132	74	½		Corpus callosum
		0.4	~0.5			3				1½	100	Internal capsule
												Septal region
8				41			158			6		Crus cerebri
		~0.15	0.4									Diencephalon
							(+ Hypothal)					(without hypothal.)
	7			10	12	6	74	157		81½	100	Thalamus (whole)
							77					Anterior nuclei
				11								Medial nuclei
				8								Lateral nuclei
29		3.3	3.5	120	102	20	~125			126½		Hypothalamus (whole)
				70								Anterior nuclei
												Intermediate nuc.
				22								Posterior nuclei
23½					5		141			40	100	Lateral geniculate
31					37		133					Medial geniculate
			0.28	68							0	Mesencephalon (whole)
54	20				55		281		570	130		Superior colliculi
27	10			20	141		180		450			Inferior colliculi
				76	119		234					Central grey matter
					699		406					Substantia nigra
42½					30		109					Red nucleus
							~150			68½		Mes. reticular form.
	27½	~0.1	~0.05	9	~0			150	290	60	100	Cerebellum (whole)
	29						~80					Cortex
17½							315					Dentate nuc.
	19			46	3		43	94	260			Pons
	½	~0		35				84	255			Medulla (whole)
6				6		3	10			1½	15	Pyramids
				60								IV Ventricle
33				110	← cun. only → 350							Nuc. cun. & grac.
				375								Area postrema
		0.4	0.4	30			16			~8½		Spinal cord (whole)
							75					Ant. horn
				14			~10				100	Ant. roots
							150					Post. horn
				42		10	~10				100	Post. roots
		8.0		14								Stellate ganglion
		10.0					0				0	Sup. cervical ganglion
				49		1	76					Optic tract
			0	7			~8			½	100	Optic nerve
		7.0	5.0	22								Vagus nerve

References
19. Harris, Jacobsohn and Kahlson (1952).
20. Harris and Holton (1953).
21. Holzbauer and Vogt (1956).
22. Kuntzman, Shore, Bogdanski and Brodie (1961).
23. Kwiatowski (1943).
24. Lowe, Robins and Eyerman (1958).
25. MacIntosh (1941).
26. Nachmansohn (1940).
27. Okinaka and Yoshikawa (1955).
28. Okinaka, Yoshikawa, Uono, Muro, Mozai, Igata, Tanabe, Ueda and Tomonaga (1961).
29. Paasonen and Vogt (1956).
30. Pernow (1953).
31. Tissot (1961).
32. Twarog and Page (1953).
33. Vogt (1954).
34. Werle and Palm (1950).
35. West (1957).
36. Zetler and Schlosser (1955).

TABLE VI. EVIDENCE FOR THE TRANSMITTER FUNCTION OF ACETYLCHOLINE IN SYMPATHETIC GANGLIA AND AT SKELETAL NEUROMUSCULAR JUNCTIONS

	Ganglia	Neuromuscular Junctions
Orthodromic stimulation giving liberation of acetylcholine	Feldberg and Gaddum (1934)	Dale, Feldberg, and Vogt (1936)
Antidromic stimulation failing to release acetylcholine	Feldberg and Vartiainen (1934)	Dale, Feldberg, and Vogt (1936)
Excitation of postsynaptic structure by injected acetylcholine	Feldberg and Gaddum (1934)	Brown, Dale, and Feldberg (1936)
Presence of cholinesterase, absent from synaptic region after denervation	von Brücke (1937)	Couteaux and Nachmansohn (1940)
Potentiation of stimulation effects by anticholinesterases	Feldberg and Vartiainen (1934)	Brown, Dale and Feldberg (1936) Bacq and Brown (1937)
Supersensitivity to injected acetylcholine after denervation	Cannon and Rosenblueth (1949)	Brown (1937)

cation) has claimed that only a small part of the material biologically identifiable as acetylcholine in ganglia is actually this chemical compound, while the larger amount is due to the presence of other non-choline esters which have similar biological actions but are chemically quite distinct. Examples of such compounds are the esters of γ-butyrobetaine (Hosein and McLennan, 1959; Chaillet, Phillipot, and Schlag, 1961). The same situation may also hold in tissues of the central nervous system (Hosein, Proulx, and Ara, 1962). In the light of this and of the fact that a number of other choline esters are also known to exist in nervous tissue, the term "cholinergic," which will be used repeatedly in the ensuing discussion, should not be taken to indicate that the chemical identification of acetylcholine as a synaptic transmitter has in fact been accomplished.

The action of pharmacological agents upon these peripheral processes is worthy of comment, for the mechanisms involved are better understood than is the case for central synapses. It is evident that in addition to the effects to be expected from interference with the normal operation of cholinesterase, pharmacological attack can be directed at three main sites: (a) the synthesis of the transmitter; (b) its release; and (c) its combination with the postsynaptic membrane. Agents which influence each of these steps are known.

(1) In 1955 Schueler described the pharmacological actions of a number of compounds which contained two quaternary ammonium groups, and suggested that one which had two choline moieties in the molecule (hemicholinium #3) might owe its action as a respiratory depressant to an interference with acetylcholine metabolism. It was subsequently demonstrated that this hemicholinium inhibits the synthesis of acetylcholine in sympathetic ganglia (MacIntosh, Birks, and Sastry, 1956, 1958) by blocking the extremely efficient uptake of choline into the cells (MacIntosh, 1959), and it thereby prevents ganglionic transmission once the preformed stores of transmitter have been exhausted by stimulation. At the neuromuscular junctions of frogs (Martin and Orkand, 1961) and of guinea pigs (Thies and Brooks, 1961), this agent apparently does not interfere either with the synthesis or with the release of acetylcholine; however, it does cause failure of the transmission process by a postsynaptic competitive block manifested by smaller end-plate potentials and a decreased sensitivity of the end-plate to applied acetylcholine. The difference in action of this hemicholinium at the two cholinergic sites is striking and illustrates the danger of extrapolation of findings from one situation to another. The reason underlying the difference is not certainly known, although the low rates of stimulation used in the neuromuscular experiments might not have been expected to deplete the stores of acetylcholine sufficiently to allow an effect upon synthesis to be evidenced, and the postsynaptic action therefore became predominant.

(2) The release of acetylcholine at the neuromuscular junction and at ganglionic synapses is prevented by a lack of calcium (Harvey and MacIntosh, 1940; del Castillo and Stark, 1952) or of sodium (Quastel and Birks, 1962) in the environmental fluid, by excess magnesium (del Castillo and Engbaek, 1954), by botulinum toxin (Burgen, Dickens, and Zatman, 1949), and by certain agents whose more striking actions are postsynaptic, of which curare (Lilleheil and Naess, 1960, 1961) and procaine (Straughan, 1961) are examples. The possible modes of action of the cations in this process have been briefly discussed earlier.

The effect of botulinum toxin in preventing acetylcholine release at neuromuscular junctions is manifested by a marked reduction in the frequency of miniature end-plate potentials, although when these are observed their amplitude and time course is normal (Brooks, 1956). Thus, there is no indication of an effect of the toxin upon the postsynaptic structure. Thesleff (1960) has observed that in light intoxication the defect can be overcome by the addition of extra calcium to the environmental fluid. If the arrival of an action potential in the presynaptic terminal causes the uptake of calcium and this in turn triggers the release of transmitter (see p. 20), it would be of great interest to know whether an antagonistic action of the toxin upon the uptake of calcium during activity in axons (Hodgkin and Keynes, 1957) could be demonstrated. The fact that no morphological changes in the internal arrangements of the endings or of the synaptic gutters occur (Thesleff, 1960) would further the concept of a chemical competition as the cause of the failure of release rather than a physical damage to the structures involved.

The local anesthetic procaine has long been known to block neuromuscular transmission, an effect attributable in large part to its curare-like action (Fulton, 1921). However, it has recently been shown by Straughan (1961) that this drug can cause a reduction of acetylcholine release in concentrations lower than those causing a curariform block, this effect being noticeable at high frequencies of stimulation when the release of acetylcholine, as estimated from the amplitude of the EPP, is already reduced (Krnjević and Miledi, 1958a). It was felt that the action of procaine was exerted directly upon the fine nerve endings and is related to its local anesthetic properties, since cocaine also has a similar action (Bülbring, 1946). The presynaptic effect of tubocurarine demonstrated by Lilleheil and Naess (1960, 1961) appears to have a similar basis.

(3) Of considerably greater pharmacological importance are those agents which prevent the action of released acetylcholine, i.e., which cause ganglionic blockade or functional paralysis by interfering with the normal postsynaptic processes. There are clearly two distinct ways in which this could occur, and drugs are known which exhibit either type of action. The drug could block the receptor sites which are normally reactive to acetylcholine and thus prevent their response to the transmitter liberated upon them; such is the mode of action of curare at neuromuscular junctions and in ganglia (Eccles, Katz, and Kuffler, 1942). The second mechanism is shown by those agents which themselves cause a long-lasting depolarization of the postsynaptic region and thus lead to excitation of the innervated structure preceding the development of block. Decamethonium is an example of such a substance active at the neuromuscular junction, and nicotine or hexamethonium in ganglia. It should be noted that an excess of acetylcholine itself will similarly produce a depolarizing block in these structures (Paton and Perry, 1953; Pascoe, 1956).

That there are subtle differences in the nature of the various types of cholinergic receptors has been implied in earlier discussions, but requires mention again here. Curare and other drugs which are potent as blockers of the "nicotinic" actions of acetylcholine are ineffective at postganglionic cholinergic synapses with target organs, while the belladonna alkaloids atropine and scopolamine, which are able completely to block these "muscarinic" effects by competition for the receptor sites, are inactive in ganglia or at skeletal neuromuscular junctions. Although the question of penetration of the drugs to the synaptic areas must not be discounted as possibly contributing in part to this difference, it is probable

also that the structures of the receptive membranes are not identical in these cases. Differences between even nicotinic synapses are indicated by the fact that ganglionic transmission is blocked by hexamethonium but unaffected by decamethonium, while the reverse is true for neuromuscular junctions.

There is evidence of a rather confusing nature that certain natural constituents of the nervous system, which in all probability function elsewhere as transmitters of synaptic action, are able markedly to affect the transmission process in synaptic ganglia. Thus, Marrazzi (1939) first showed and others have confirmed (for references see Goffart, 1957) that the intravenous administration of adrenaline to cats would depress the postganglionic response of the superior cervical ganglion, and the effect is clearly observable following a dose as small as 5 μg (M. C. L. Weir and H. McLennan, unpublished observations). A similar but less marked effect can be obtained with noradrenaline (Lundberg, 1952). Other authors (Bülbring and Burn, 1942; Konzett, 1950; Malméjac, 1955) have stated that sufficiently small doses of adrenaline are not depressant but actually enhance the response of the ganglion, both to electrical stimulation and following the injection of acetylcholine, but this has not been a universal observation (Lundberg, 1952; Eccles and Libet, 1961; Weir and McLennan). There are thus conflicting data for which the causes of discrepancy are not certain. A further complication, but in which there may be a partial explanation of some of the differing results, is provided by the findings of Kewitz and Reinert (1954a). They have found that both adrenaline and noradrenaline, in small doses, enhanced the effectiveness of injected acetylcholine but reduced the response obtained by preganglionic stimulation.

A lack of consistency is apparent also in the results of those who have attempted to block the actions of injected adrenaline upon ganglionic transmission. Konzett (1950), who tested dibenamine, and Matthews (1956) with dibenzyline, failed to find a blocking action of these drugs, while on the other hand Eccles and Libet (1961) and Weir and McLennan found them to be effective in the prevention of the adenraline depression. Again, the reason for the discrepancies is not clear. Evidently, however, the endogenous catecholamines are capable of influencing events at these cholinergic synapses, and Bülbring (1944) has further reported that an adrenaline-like material is actually released from the perfused ganglion following presynaptic stimulation.

Histamine has also been claimed to enhance ganglionic transmission (Konzett, 1952), although the action is not an impressive one. This substance is said to be released from tissues by adrenaline (Staub, 1946), and *vice versa* (as in the well-known clinical test for pheochromocytoma). It is perhaps reasonable to assume, therefore, that this may serve to explain the effect of histamine upon ganglionic transmission.

Eccles and Libet (1961) have studied the electrical responses of curarized ganglia in an attempt to account for these and other observations, and their hypothesis may be summarized by Figure 6.1. They believe that adrenaline is liberated from chromaffin cells which are known to be present in sympathetic ganglia and to receive preganglionic innervation, and the released adrenaline in turn is felt to affect the ganglion cells themselves by producing a positive potential change. This wave (the P wave) will result in the reduction of the size of the postganglionic response if it is produced in a non-curarized preparation. Exogenously applied adrenaline is therefore believed to act by the production of such positivity. The size of the P wave was found to be reduced by atropine, as is the "late negative" (LN) wave, also observed in these ganglia; so that the synapses upon the chromaffin cells and upon the ganglion cells leading to the LN wave are felt to be distinct from those yielding the earlier negative (N) potential, which in non-curarized preparations leads to the discharge of the neurones. This last process is, of course, unaffected by atropine.

This hypothesis will adequately account for the depression of the ganglionic response

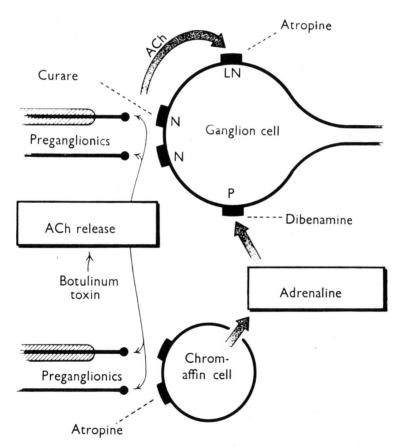

Figure 6.1. A diagram to illustrate the possible sites of action of transmitter substances and blocking agents in mammalian sympathetic ganglia. Receptor sites for the transmitter substances are shown as small blocks on the cell membranes, but their represented localizations are of on significance. The letters *P*, *N*, and *LN* refer to the positive, negative, and late negative phases of the compound potential recorded from curarized ganglia. (From Eccles and Libet, 1961, by permission of the Journal of Physiology.)

by adrenaline, but cannot explain the observations of Bülbring and Burn (1942) and of others who have found enhanced ganglionic transmission in the presence of suitably low doses of the substance. This latter effect is more in accord with results obtained in skeletal muscle, in which the injection of adrenaline usually gives rise to an enhanced contraction (see, e.g., Brown, Goffart, and Vianna Dias, 1950). Krnjević and Miledi (1958b) have further investigated this effect and have shown that there are several contributing factors. Adrenaline increased the size of an EPP evoked by nerve stimulation, but not that produced by the local application of acetylcholine to an end-plate, which indicated that its action was to bring about a larger liberation of transmitter from the presynaptic terminals in response to each nerve volley. This conclusion was supported also by the observed increase in frequency of miniature EPP's in the presence of adrenaline. Secondly, the excitability of the muscle membrane tended to be reduced by adrenaline, and the balance between these oppositely directed influences determined the final result of the application. Finally, there is clear evidence of an enhanced contractile response (Brown, Bülbring, and Burns, 1948). The fact that there are two oppositely directed actions upon the electrical response of neuromuscular synapses may also provide an explanation for the differences observed following the injection of adrenaline into sympathetic ganglia. Krnjević and Miledi (1958b) emphasized that in muscle the observed effects are somewhat unpredictable and that the predominance of the enhancing presynaptic action or of the depressant postsynaptic action will determine the end result. Analogous experiments to show whether a similar state of affairs occurs in ganglia have not been performed.

These actions of adrenaline upon peripheral cholinergic synapses have been discussed at some length, since it must be considered that there is a very real possibility that similar effects occur also in the central nervous system.

There are a great many agents available whose action is to inhibit the activity of that cholinesterase, the principal function of which is to destroy liberated acetylcholine. The response of a muscle to maximal stimulation of its motor nerve is enhanced in the presence of such an agent because of the repetitive activation of the synapses, and this can be correlated with the persistence of acetylcholine in the system (Brown, 1937). A similar type of action may be expected at all other cholinergic synapses where the inactivation of acetylcholine by cholinesterase is the primary means by which termination of effect occurs. But if physical diffusion away from the site of action is the first step, then anticholinesterase drugs may have little or no influence upon the transmission process. Such may be the explanation of their small effect in sympathetic ganglia for example (Emmelin and MacIntosh, 1956).

Thus far we have considered the probable mechanism of acetylcholine at synapses where its intimate connection with transmission can hardly be doubted; however, there are certain indications that the substance may play a role also at other synapses where it is not the principal transmitting agent, just as the catecholamines, as described above, may influence transmission at cholinergic sites. The evidence stems in part from the histochemical localization of cholinesterase, to which reference has been made; and the theory which has been proposed to account for these and other observations and which postulates a wider role for acetylcholine at many synaptic junctions has recently been reviewed by Koelle (1962).

Briefly, the histochemical data are these. Neurones whose effects are certainly transmitted by acetylcholine, e.g., those of the ciliary ganglion, are heavily stained for cholinesterase, as are the preganglionic fibers which impinge upon them (Koelle and Koelle, 1959). In the stellate ganglion, on the other hand, only a few such densely staining cells are found, and these presumably give rise to sympathetic cholinergic vasodilator fibers. The great majority of the cells stain only very faintly and are likely to be those of the sympathetic postganglionic fibers, which liberate an adrenergic transmitter from their endings. Similar reports of the light staining for cholinesterase of other neurones known to be non-cholinergic have been made in a number of animal species and from a variety of sites. In all cases the enzyme has been shown to be associated with neurones and not with glia.

The pharmacological correlates of these observations stem, for ganglia, from the findings of Burn and his colleagues. These workers have shown: (a) that after administration of sufficient atropine to block the effects of injected acetylcholine, a dose of this substance produces sympathomimetic action (Burn and Rand, 1958a,b,); (b) that in an animal treated with reserpine, which depletes the endogenous stores of catecholamines, sympathetic stimulation gives rise to cholinomimetic responses, which can be blocked by atropine (Burn and Rand, 1960); (c) that acetylcholine or nicotine, which cause pilomotor responses upon intradermal injection or cause the isolated nictitating membrane to contract, fail to do so in animals pretreated with reserpine (Burn, Leach, Rand, and Thompson, 1959); and (d) that certain effect of stimulation of sympathetic fibers can be prevented by hemicholinium #3, which prevents the synthesis of acetylcholine (Chang and Rand, 1960). The conclusion was drawn that acetylcholine is involved in the mediation of adrenergic effects and that, as in case (b), where an adrenergic response is no longer possible, acetylcholine can be seen to be released upon stimulation of synaptic fibers.

Evidence for an action of acetylcholine upon the presynaptic endings at neuromuscular junctions was obtained originally by Masland and Wigton (1940). They showed that the fasciculation in muscle, induced by the anticholinesterase drug eserine, occasioned bursts of antidromic impulses in the motor axons. Although their interpretation of this observation, namely, that the accumulation of acetylcholine resulting from the drug could excite the motor nerve terminals, has been questioned, more recent evidence has confirmed it (Werner, 1961). Other indications which point in the same direction have been cited in the review by Koelle (1962), and his conclusions drawn therefrom are as follow. At all synapses, cholinergic and non-cholinergic, the arrival of an action potential in the presynaptic ending causes the release of a small number of quanta of acetylcholine, and this material acts upon the presynaptic membrane to cause the liberation of the "true" synaptic transmitter. This may be either acetylcholine itself (at cholinergic synapses) or some other substance, and it is this secondarily released material which crosses the synaptic cleft to produce the characteristic graded potential in the postsynaptic structure. The scheme is illustrated by Figure 6.2. Interference with the release either of acetylcholine or of the "true" transmitter would effectively block the synapse.

The evidence for the proposed mechanism is derived largely from studies of peripheral synapses, although Koelle (1954) has noted that the majority of central nervous system neurones also show faint staining for cholinesterase; and de Lorenzo (1961) (see p.

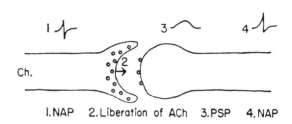

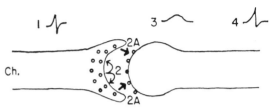

1. NAP   2. Liberation of ACh   3. PSP   4. NAP

Figure 6.2. Diagrams to indicate the possible role of acetylcholine in cholinergic transmission. Above: the "standard" concept, in which acetylcholine is released (step 2) from the presynaptic terminal and diffuses across the synaptic cleft to produce a postsynaptic potential (3). Below: the newer concept proposed by Koelle, in which the first acetylcholine released (2) acts upon the presynaptic terminal to cause the further release of transmitter (2A), which only then diffuses across the cleft to produce postsynaptic membrane changes. *NAP:* nerve action potential. (From Koelle, 1962, by permission of the Journal of Pharmacy and Pharmacology.)

8) has demonstrated its localization to the synaptic areas of some cortical cells. Since known central cholinergic neurones, such as motoneurones, stain as heavily as the cells of parasympathetic ganglia, it may be presumed that the situation at lightly staining cells is analogous to that in the stellate ganglion; and Koelle would therefore extend his hypothesis to include the synapses upon some cells, at any rate, of the central nervous system. He has noted that the patterns are different in different animals; that, for example, the mechanism would seem to be a more general one in the rabbit and monkey than in the cat. The evidence for its widespread occurrence is, however, very slight, and it is better to confine our consideration to the situation at the endings of postganglionic sympathetic fibers, since parasympathetic endings and neuromuscular junctions are certainly cholinergic in nature, and the analysis of a possible two-stage process there is somewhat uncertain.

In the light of what has been said about the presently accepted concept of the release of transmitter, the advantages to be derived from a mechanism of this type are not immediately apparent. The prior release of acetylcholine as a triggering device for the subsequent liberation of the "true" transmitter would seem to introduce an unnecessary complication into the whole process, and in the case of non-cholinergic synapses to require that a neurone manufacture and store both agents. There is little doubt that the adrenergic transmitter is contained within the nerve terminals, since preganglionic nerve section leads to depletion of the material (von Euler and Purkhold, 1951).

One possible explanation, at least of the histochemical data, is that the presence of cholinesterase in non-cholinergic situations is quite accidental, i.e., that the protein exists there as part of the structural matrix of the cell and that it also has enzymatic properties is a functionally unimportant fact. The widespread distribution of cholinesterase in areas of the central nervous system which contain little acetylcholine or cholinacetylase (Table V) would tend to substantiate this view, and there is evidence that about 50 per cent of the cholinesterase of muscle is due to its myosin content (Varga, Kövér, Kovács, and Hetényi, 1957), which would again indicate that its ability to hydrolyze acetylcholine is coincidental. Nevertheless, the findings of Burn and Rand require explanation, and Koelle's hypothesis provides a plausible one. The question of its applicability to structures other than postganglionic sympathetic endings must remain open.

It remains to discuss briefly the matter of the specificity of the response of various excitable structures to acetylcholine, since to some extent such specificity is implicit in the original enunciation of the mechanism of chemical synaptic transmission. One does not, however, need to seek far in order to find structures which respond to the application of small amounts of acetylcholine, even though these structures do not receive a physiological cholinergic innervation. The probability is also that other synaptic transmitter substances are similarly capable of activating structures when applied exogenously, and the danger of misinterpretation of experimental data in favor of a transmitter role for the substance at that site, when in fact it has no physiological function there, must be emphasized.

Perhaps the clearest example of this pharmacological type of action of acetylcholine is rendered by its effects upon the peripheral endings of primary sensory neurones (Brown and Gray, 1948); and an action of the substance upon sensory axons themselves, which is also probably not of physiological significance, has been demonstrated by Douglas and Ritchie (1960). Capillary dilatation in the rabbit's ear may be brought about by the injection of as little as 10^{-10} g of acetylcholine (Armin and Grant, 1953), and the dilatation produced greatly resembles that brought about by antidromic stimulation of the sensory fibers supplying the ear. However, the effect of injected acetylcholine, but not that of the stimulation, can be prevented by atropine (Holton and Perry, 1951), and the conclusion would be that acetylcholine is not normally involved in this process of antidromic vasodilatation (for a further discussion of this topic, see p. 91). There is abundant evidence also (for references see Witzleb, 1959) that many other types of sensory receptor are sensitive to acetylcholine, but in no case has a firm indication that sensory neurones are cholinergic, in vertebrates at any rate, been forthcoming; and indeed, most authors would accept that these are unquestionably non-cholinergic in function. The possibility that injected acetylcholine does not exactly mimic the effects of nerve stimulation, even in cholinergic structures (Kewitz and Reinert, 1954a,b), to which reference has been made on p. 69, must, however, always be kept in mind during interpretation of such data.

Nevertheless, the probabilities are that in some situations acetylcholine is capable of initiating changes in excitable tissue cells in an unspecific manner, in the sense that specialized receptors for this substance can hardly be regarded as occurring upon cells which do not normally receive a cholinergic nerve supply. There are other indications too of a general unspecificity of receptor patches even at synaptic areas. The most striking example is that provided by the experiments of de Castro (1951), in which he demonstrated that a functional union could be established between non-cholinergic afferent fibers in the vagus and the cholinergic neurones of the superior cervical ganglion, and on pharmacological grounds he concluded that the newly established synapses were mediated by the non-cholinergic transmitter. This conclusion has been questioned by Matsumara and Koelle (1961), who do, however, state that the staining for cholinesterase shown by the new presynaptic fibers is light in comparison to that found in normal preganglionic axons. The implication is that the subsynaptic regions of the cells of the ganglion, which normally respond to the release of acetylcholine as a synaptic transmitter, have now become sensitive to a different transmitter substance.

In the vertebrate central nervous system, there is only one synapse identified whose operation can, with assurance, be ascribed to acetylcholine. The Renshaw cells of the anterior horn of the spinal cord receive innervation from collateral branches of the motor axons, the terminals of which appear as typical boutons (Szentágothai, 1958). Since the transmitter substance liberated at the neuromuscular junctions is acetylcholine, it is not surprising that that shown to be released at the Renshaw cell synapses is the same compound (Eccles, Fatt, and Koketsu, 1954; Eccles, Eccles, and Fatt, 1956; Curtis and Eccles, 1958a,b). This demonstration, incidentally, provides the only proof yet known for the validity of the hypothesis put forward by Dale (1935) (and to which further reference will be made) to the effect that a given nerve fiber releases the same transmitter substance at all of its endings. The evidence which substantiates the cholinergic nature of this synapse is briefly as follows. Renshaw cells are excited by the intra-arterial or iontophoretic application of acetylcholine. Their response to synaptic stimulation is increased

and their threshold for acetylcholine reduced by anticholinesterase drugs and their response to stimulation is markedly depressed by cholinergic-blocking agents. Although some of the criteria listed on page 23 have not been fulfilled, the probability that the excitatory synapses upon Renshaw cells are cholinergic in nature is clearly very strong. It must be noted also that all the effects of acetylcholine upon the cord cannot be explained by its actions upon the Renshaw cells alone, and it seems probable that other unidentified cholinergic synapses must exist (Fernandez de Molina, Gray, and Palmer, 1958).

There are a number of points in connection with these results which are worthy of mention, for they emphasize the difficulties inherent in any attempt to identify the transmitters of central synapses. In the case of the Renshaw cells it appears that two barriers exist between the systemic circulation and the postsynaptic regions of the cell surface. One is the well-recognized blood-brain barrier, and the second is the "synaptic barrier" believed to surround the axonal endings and synaptic areas of the postsynaptic neurone (Figure 6.3). The evidence for the existence of a real barrier between blood and the tissue fluids of the brain need not be reviewed here (see, e.g.,

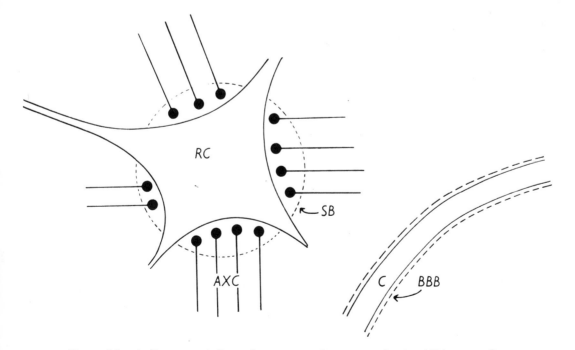

Figure 6.3. A diagram to indicate the presence of a synaptic barrier (*SB*) surrounding a Renshaw cell (*RC*) and preventing the diffusion away of the acetylcholine released at the endings of the motor axon collaterals (*AXC*); *C*, a capillary surrounded by the blood-brain barrier (*BBB*). (From Curtis and Eccles, 1958b, by permission of the Journal of Physiology.)

Davson, 1957); for present purposes it is sufficient to note that certain drugs active at peripheral cholinergic sites are unable to penetrate into the central nervous system and affect cells there; these include such quaternary ammonium compounds as curare and prostigmine (Eccles, Eccles, and Fatt, 1956). By contrast, when these drugs were applied iontophoretically to the neighborhood of the cells, they respectively exhibited their expected blocking and anticholinesterase actions. Anticholinesterases (eserine) or curariform drugs (dihydro-β-erythroidine) which are tertiary amines are unimpeded by the barrier. The distinction between the quaternary and tertiary compounds so far as their central actions are concerned was first described by Crum-Brown and Fraser in 1869.

The second barrier is less well understood; however, its existence has been considered earlier as explaining the very long-lasting repetitive discharge of the Renshaw cells to single volleys, and it has been found by Curtis and Eccles (1958b) that it is not possible to excite such high frequency discharges by the local application of acetylcholine to the cell. The implication is that, as indicated by Figure 6.3, a physiological barrier at once prevents acetylcholine liberated from the presynaptic endings to escape from the synaptic regions and be destroyed, and at the same time allows only a small amount of artificially applied material to reach the receptive areas. Pointing in the same direction is the finding of Eccles, Fatt, and Koketsu (1954) that drugs which are active in depressing the response of the cell to synaptic activation are never capable of preventing the first two discharges in the train (cf. also Figure 6.7). Again one must assume a barrier impeding the entrance of the drug to the receptor areas of the synapse. Although this particular type of barrier has been demonstrated clearly only for Renshaw cells, it is likely to be of widespread occurrence in the central nervous system, and may be suspected to exist in any situation in which a neurone responds by repetitive firing to a single presynaptic volley. It is evident, therefore, that negative results obtained with any drug must always be regarded with some caution, particularly if the agent has been administered systemically.

The actions of acetylcholine and of drugs which influence its normal effects upon higher centers of the central nervous system have been widely investigated, and the earlier work was ably reviewed by Feldberg (1945).

Inasmuch as acetylcholine, which is itself a quaternary ammonium compound, may be impeded in its progress through the blood-brain barrier, the effects which some authors have observed following systemic administration of large doses, such as those obtained by Cohen, Thale, and Tissenbaum (1944), may well be due secondarily to circulatory changes. Dikshit (1934) and many others following him have injected the substance into the cerebral ventricles. Such experiments have, in general, yielded marked autonomic effects and behavioral changes in the direction of sleep, bewilderment, or stupor, which suggests that acetylcholine was having an inhibitory, rather than an excitatory, action. Similar reactions were observed by Feldberg and Sherwood (1954b) following the administration of anticholinesterase drugs. The site of these actions would appear to be in the hypothalamus and reticular formation of the tegmentum; and in confirmation of this, the excitatory effects of tubocurarine injections have been definitely localized to this area (Feldberg and Malcolm, 1959). Feldberg and Malcolm interpreted their tubocurarine results as due to a direct excitatory effect of the drug upon neurones rather than to a blocking of cholinergic action (cf. also Chang, 1953), and noted further that tremorous movements suppressed by adrenaline or by noradrenaline were also produced following the tubocurarine administration. There seems, however, little reason to believe that the effects observed may not have been due to a block of acetylcholine responses.

There are a number of confusing reports on the development of a catatonic state in animals after intracerebral acetylcholine administration. Sherwood (1952) stated that the intraventricular injection of large amounts would produce catatonia and that the effect was more easily observed in animals with lesions between the upper tegmentum and the posterior hypothalamus. On the other hand, van Andel and Ernst (1961) report that the catatonia produced by tryptamine injection is prevented by eserine and intensified by atropine, and they describe this as a "cholinergic hypofunction." The relationship of these results to one another is not clear, but they would seem to be diametrically opposite.

The tegmental and hypothalamic areas of the brain which are mentioned above are, of course, not the only ones which contain acetylcholine and the enzyme systems responsible for its synthesis and ultimate destruction. It may be reasonably suspected that those regions which contain the highest concentrations are the sites of conglomerations of cholinergic neurones; and the finding, for example, that such an area of high concentration was the medical thalamus led Feldberg to suggest that an alternation of cholinergic with non-cholinergic neurones in the long pathways of the central nervous system may occur. However, no more precise identification of these postulated cholinergic synapses has been made. Of the criteria given on page 23, some cannot be definitely satisfied, in part because of the anatomical complexies of the brain and in part because of the technical impossibility of, for example, carrying out a local perfusion of an area with the intention of identifying in the perfusate substances released during stimulation. There is, however, a very high probability that acetylcholine does function as a transmitter at central synapses other than the spinal cord synapse described on p. 79, and that pharmacological agents which are active at peripheral cholinergic synapses are able to exert effects by the same mechanisms in the central nervous system, provided always that they are able to reach the correct sites.

There remains, as an experimental approach, the iontophoretic application of acetylcholine to single neurones of the central nervous system, a technique which has been successfully used by Curtis and his colleagues in investigations of the spinal cord. Such studies have, to date, been carried out only upon neurones in the brain stem (Curtis and Koizumi, 1961), and have yielded disappointingly negative results. Neurones in the reticular formation of the medulla and mesencephalon were never found to be excited by acetylcholine. Furthermore, the majority of reticular formation cells studied were spontaneously active and acetylcholine appeared not to have any inhibitory action upon them, such as was suggested above might be the case for the more rostral parts of the reticular formation. The only cells found to be excited by an application were some in the inferior colliculi, and these were scattered among other cells which were unresponsive. Curtis and Koizumi concluded that the excitation was not such as would have been expected if acetylcholine were acting as a synaptic transmitter, and the functional significance of these observations therefore remains uncertain. It may be noted (Table V) that the inferior colliculus is a region of only moderate cholinacetylase content.

Acetylcholine is a substance widely distributed in nature, and its presence need not signify the existence of nerve cells or endings; thus, for example, it occurs in both spleen and placenta of mammals. It has been identified, at least by biological tests, in many invertebrates; but in spite of this its function as a synaptic transmitter has been firmly established in only four instances. These are at the neuromuscular junctions of the longitudinal muscle of *Hirudo medicinalis* (Bacq and Coppée, 1937a,b) and of the retractor muscle of *Stichopus regalis* (Bacq, 1939), at the synapse between the cardio-inhibitory fibers and the heart of *Venus mercenaria* (Prosser, 1940; Welsh, 1953), and at some inhibitory synapses in the abdominal ganglion of *Aplysia depilans* (Tauc and Gerschenfeld, 1960, 1962). In all other instances where actions of applied acetylcholine have been demonstrated, actions which may be potentiated or blocked by appropriate drugs, no final evidence exists to prove that the material has a physiological role to play. The actions of acetylcholine at mammalian sites where it can clearly be shown not to have a physiological function, which have been discussed above, provide an eloquent enough reason for caution in the ascription of transmitter action.

In spite of the fact that two of the authenticated cases of cholinergic transmission in invertebrates are at neuromuscular junctions and are thus analogous to the situation in vertebrates, this is not a general rule. Thus, acetylcholine has no action upon the somatic musculature of crustacea (Bacq, 1935; Ellis, Thienes, and Wiersma, 1942), and drugs such as curare have no influence upon neuromuscular transmission in these animals. Although the peripheral nerve trunks of crustacea contain acetylcholine, this has now been shown to be exclusively, in all likelihood, confined to the sensory axons (Florey and Biederman, 1960), and cholinergic sensory transmission within the central nervous system would seem to be probable, although this point has not been established directly. Florey and Biederman explain the earlier observations of Florey and Florey (1954) on the rapid contraction of crayfish muscle following injection of acetylcholine as possibly due to activation of the sensory system with a resultant reflex muscle response brought about by secondary stimulation of the motor axons.

The effects of acetylcholine upon the hearts of mollusks has been examined by many workers (for references see Florey, 1961) and, as mentioned above, the function of acetyl-choline as an inhibitory transmitter in the heart of *Venus mercenaria* has been established. Its action however is not invariably inhibitory in animals of this phylum. Thus, Florey and Merwin (1961), for example, have shown that acceleration leading to systolic arrest occurs in *Mytilus californianus*. Whether these are actions upon the heart muscle itself or are mediated by ganglion cells is not clear, although no neurones have been described in the Venus heart (Prosser, 1940). In other cases it is not certain whether acetylcholine can be regarded as physiologically involved in cardiac regulation. Thus, Jaeger (1961) has shown that, although acetylcholine excites the heart of *Strophocheilos oblongus*, an extract of the heart contains an excitatory substance which is not acetylcholine.

There have also been many studies of the hearts of crustacea in which a neurogenic origin of the beat is unquestioned (for references see Florey, 1960b). In these genera, acetylcholine invariably causes a cardiac acceleration (Welsh, 1939a, and many others), and Welsh (1939b) further showed that extracts of the nervous system could cause acceleration of the heart indistinguishable from that due to acetylcholine or to stimulation of the cardio-accelerator nerves. In spite of this evidence, it is now likely that one has to deal here with yet another "pharmacological" action of acetylcholine, for not only do atropine and eserine, respectively, block and potentiate the effects of applied acetylcholine without influencing the actions of nerve stimulation, but the accelerator nerves and the heart ganglia (of *Homarus americanus*, at least) do not contain any acetylcholine (Florey, 1961). It appears, therefore, that the concept of a cholinergic mechanism responsible for cardiac control in these animals in untenable.

In the *Aplysia* ganglia, Tauc and Gerschenfeld (1962) have assembled a body of data for the existence of cholinergic inhibitory synapses which is very impressive. They have been able to show that, in those cells which receive an inhibitory supply, acetylcholine causes an hyperpolarization and that the equilibrium potential for this process is identical to that found for the physiological inhibition. Furthermore, atropine and curare block both the action of applied acetylcholine and the natural inhibitory process, and its role as the inhibitory synaptic transmitter is very probable.

CATECHOLAMINES

The discovery by Elliott (1904, 1905) of the striking resemblance of the effects of administered adrenaline to those of sympathetic nerve stimulation, which laid the basis for later development of the concept of the chemical transmission of synaptic events, has been described above. Elliott's (1905) conclusions that are particularly appropriate here may be quoted:

"In all vertebrates the reaction of any plain muscle to adrenalin is of a similar character to that following excitation of the sympathetic (thoracico-lumbar) visceral nerves supplying that muscle. The change may be either to contraction or relaxation. In default of sympathetic innervation, plain muscle is indifferent to adrenalin.

"A positive reaction to adrenalin is a trustworthy proof of the existence and nature of sympathetic nerves in any organ.

"Plain muscle, when denervated, shows increase of the capacity for irritation by adrenalin than it had previously possessed.

"Sympathetic nerve cells with their fibres, and the contractile muscle fibres are not irritated by adrenalin, the stimulation takes place at the junction of muscle and nerve."

The correspondence of the effects of stimulation and of administered adrenaline, while close, was recognized as being not perfect; and Barger and Dale (1910) noted that some other catecholamines, particularly noradrenaline (which had been synthesized by Stolz in 1904), more closely imitated the actions of nerve stimulation than did adrenaline itself. Cannon and Uridil (1921) reported that the action of the substance released into a perfusate during stimulation of the hepatic nerves was not adrenaline, and in 1933 Cannon and Rosenblueth suggested the term "sympathin" to represent the substance active physiologically and released from adrenergic nerve endings but which was to be regarded as distinct from adrenaline itself. Many other workers over the years recognized that noradrenaline more nearly corresponded to sympathin than did adrenaline, but it was not until 1948 that von Euler was able positively to identify the substance in adrenergic nerve fibers, while slightly earlier Holtz, Credner, and Kroneberg (1947) demonstrated the existence in urine of a conjugate of noradrenaline and found the substance itself in the adrenal glands.

On the basis of this and of many other experiments (for details see von Euler, 1955), there can be little doubt that the majority of postganglionic sympathetic nerve fibers liberate noradrenaline as the characteristic transmitter of their effects, although, as in the case of acetylcholine, the identification has in almost all instances rested upon biological rather than chemical characterization of the material. It also appears likely that in most instances a small amount of adrenaline is released together with noradrenaline; however, since the proportion of the total sympathomimetic activity which can be ascribed to adrenaline is rather variable, it most probably does not derive from the nerve endings themselves but from chromaffin cells which are also synaptically innervated, and whose activation results in the liberation of this material (compare Figure 6.1). To the possible role of dopamine as a mediator of synaptic events we shall return later.

There are certain evident differences in the general metabolism of the catecholamines as compared with acetylcholine, one of the most striking being the appearance of sympathomimetic activity in the blood following sympathetic nerve stimulation and the presence in the urine of conjugates and oxidation products of noradrenaline. It follows, therefore, that the enzymatic inactivation of liberated catecholamines is not the rapid and efficient process which is a characteristic of cholinesterase action. Koelle (1959) has listed four main enzymatic routes by which the catecholamines are inactivated: (a) oxidative deamination by monoamine oxidase; (b) oxidation by cytochrome and tyrosine oxidases; (c) conjugation to a glucuronide or sulphate; and (d) methylation by catechol-O-methyl transferase. There is considerable argument as to which of these pathways is quantitatively the most important (see, e.g., Zeller, 1959), but the point is not of great consequence here, for it is certain that the enzymatic inactivation by any of these pathways cannot account for the rapid removal of a liberated transmitter from the site of synaptic effects. It seems much more probable than at adrenergic sites a diffusion away from the primary locus of action must occur and that the final disposal of the compound is made at a distance and at some considerable time after its synaptic liberation.

The hormonal actions of adrenaline also do not concern us here, although they evidently contribute heavily to the over-all sympathetic reaction, in which the influence of circulating adrenaline upon the response of the skeletal musculature has been adequately considered

on p. 76. It is obvious that such widespread effects could not be obtained in the presence of an inactivating mechanism of the cholinesterase type.

The nature of the postsynaptic receptor sites with which the catecholamines react has received considerable study. It is evident that at least two types of reaction are possible, which, broadly speaking, lead to excitatory or inhibitory responses, and the available information would indicate the existence of two types of receptor corresponding to these actions. The extent of reaction of the various catecholamines with the different receptors is variable: noradrenaline has actions predominantly of an excitatory nature; adrenaline is able to react with both types; while isopropylnoradrenaline apparently is effective only at the inhibitory synapses. On this basis and as the result of considerable pharmacological investigation, Ahlquist in 1948 proposed the division of peripheral adrenergic receptors into alpha and beta types, corresponding in most instances to excitatory and inhibitory actions, although this is not invariably the case. The two types of receptor are also differently blocked by a number of agents. The common adrenergic-blocking agents dibenzyline, dibenamine, and the phenothiazines act almost exclusively on the alpha receptors, while the dichloro analogue of isopropylnoradrenaline is a specific antagonist of the beta type (Powell and Slater, 1958). There is some indication that this division of the receptors into two categories may be too simplified, and Furchgott (1959) modified Ahlquist's original proposal to include four different types of receptor. Although the question is not finally settled, the existence of both alpha and beta receptors in the same tissue would seem to explain many of the anomalies which led to the proposal that more than two types actually occur (Furchgott, 1960).

For those receptors which are blocked by dibenamine at least, there is evidence that the process of their activation requires an electrostatic interaction between receptor molecule and the ammonium group of the catecholamine and therefore that the receptors must possess a negative charge (Belleau, 1960). The various blocking agents presumably act by neutralizing the charge and thus preventing the interaction of amine and receptor. Belleau (1960) has some further information on the probable nature of the anionic receptor group involved. Noting that adrenaline is an efficient catalyst of the change of adenosine triphosphate (ATP) into cyclic 3', 5'-adenosine monophosphate (Rall and Sutherland, 1959; Sutherland and Rall, 1960) and that the latter is a potent activator of phosphorylase and therefore of glycogenolysis, he suggested that ATP, bound as a cofactor, and presenting a negatively charged oxygen atom upon the phosphate group, would appear to satisfy the requirements as the receptor molecule. In addition, if the negative charge upon the oxygen were neutralized by ion pair formation with adrenaline, the cyclization and ejection of pyrophosphate would be greatly facilitated. This hypothesis is consistent with the known facts of the case and accounts satisfactorily for the well-known glycogenolytic effect of circulating adrenaline.

There is good evidence that the contraction of smooth muscle in response to sympathetic nerve stimulation takes place by the release thereupon of noradrenaline. The summation of individual unitary potentials which gives rise eventually to a threshold postsynaptic potential capable of initiating an action potential is precisely analogous to the mechanism operating in skeletal muscle (Burnstock and Holman; 1961, 1962b). The situation is, however, more complicated by reason of the facts that smooth muscle *in vitro* can contract without depolarization of the cells (Furchgott, 1960) and can still respond even if complete depolarization by a high potassium solution is produced (Evans, Schild, and Thesleff, 1958). The conclusion must therefore be that the catecholamines (and acetylcholine) are, under these conditions, able to affect directly the contractile mechanism in addition to their ability to cause membrane depolarization. The importance of this to the normal physiological function of the tissues, if any, is unknown.

Investigations into the central actions of the catecholamines and of their possible roles there as synaptic transmitters are hampered by the same difficulties as were described above for acetylcholine. The undoubted existence of an efficient blood-brain barrier (Weil-Malherbe, Axelrod, and Tomchick, 1959; Weil-Malherbe, Whitby, and Axelrod, 1961) for both adrenaline and noradrenaline renders it unlikely that these materials pass into the brain in appreciable amounts or in reasonable times after systemic administration. The only area of significant penetration is the hypothalamus, where the content of noradrenaline is conspicuously high (Table V). In addition, the uncertainty of the part played in observed responses by the vascular changes following adrenaline or noradrenaline injection complicates the picture, and this point cannot be considered settled (see the discussions in Vane, 1960). However, most workers would appear to accept the fact that direct influences upon central neurones can occur in these circumstances.

It is evident from Table V that, although both noradrenaline and dopamine are present widely in the central nervous system, areas with high concentrations are few, and, furthermore, ones that contain much of one do not necessarily contain the other also in large amount, as might perhaps be expected since dopamine is the metabolic precursor of noradrenaline. Thus, the latter has its region of highest concentration in the hypothalamus and the grey areas which surround the aqueduct, while dopamine is found in greatest amount in the telencephalic basal ganglia. In view of this lack of parallelism, the possibility that dopamine itself may play a role in synaptic processes must be considered, although this has not been commonly accepted in the past. Holtz (1960) has remarked that in the caudate nucleus and putamen and in some other organs, "dopamine itself is the end product of biosynthesis,"[*] and that its localization in these nervous structures indicates its importance for the function of the extrapyramidal system.

In the spinal cord, actions of the catecholamines have been observed which appear to indicate an influence upon neurones; however, the effects which have been obtained by various authors are not entirely consistent. Schweitzer and Wright (1937) described the effect of the intravenous administration of large doses of adrenaline (200 to 400 μg in cats) upon the knee-jerk reflex and showed that a long-lasting depression was produced which was usually preceded by an enhancement during the period of blood pressure change. This result has been essentially confirmed by Sigg, Ochs, and Gerard (1955), by ten Cate, Boeles, and Biersteker (1959) and by McLennan (1961a). Sigg, Ochs, and Gerard demonstrated, however, that the effect observed depended upon the depth of anesthesia and that it could be replaced by facilitation of the reflex when anesthesia was lightened. Bernhard, Skoglund, and Therman

---

[*]In Lunge, Leber, Darm und in bestimmten Arealen des Gehirns — im Nucl. caudatus und Putamen — ist Dopamin selbst das Endprodukt der Biosynthese . . . Die Lokalisation im Nucl. caudatus und Putamen spricht dafür, dass ihm Bedeutung für die Funktionen des extrapyramidalen Systems zukommt.

(1947); Bernhard, Gray, and Widén (1953); and Bernhard and Skoglund (1953) found that monosynaptic extensor reflexes were enhanced, while flexor reflexes were largely unaffected, by intravenous or intra-arterial injection of adrenaline in spinal cats; and this was associated with an increased positivity in the ventral roots indicative of an enhanced motoneuronal depolarization. These and other experiments (Bonvallet and Minz, 1938; Bülbring and Burn, 1941) seem, in summary, to imply that the depressant actions are confined to the spinal cord and further that they may involve a cholinergic link since they can be blocked by atropine. Potentiation, on the other hand, depends upon higher centers of the central nervous system and is more easily affected by anesthetic agents. In the experiments of Sigg, Ochs, and Gerard (1955) and of McLennan (1961a), noradrenaline had a less marked effect than adrenaline, and McLennan failed to find any action of dopamine except in the presence of an inhibitor of monoamine oxidase, when a slight depression of the knee-jerk was detected. McLennan also reported that the depressions following intravenous administration of the catecholamines could be prevented by the alpha-blocking agents dibenzyline and chlorpromazine.

These effects have been attributed to a direct action of the agents upon nerve cells and can unquestionably be distinguished from vascular changes and from actions upon the neuromuscular transmission process (Schweitzer and Wright, 1937). On the other hand, it is known that the uptake of adrenaline and noradrenaline from the blood into most areas of the central nervous system is negligible, which would render direct neuronal activity less likely; and Curtis, Eccles, and Eccles (1957), who injected the substances intra-arterially and found only a slight potentiation of spinal reflex activity after a long latency, concluded that the change was due only to local vascular effects. More recently, Curtis, Phillis, and Watkins (1961a) have applied both adrenaline and noradrenaline to spinal interneurones and have found them to be ineffective. In these experiments, the blood-brain barrier is circumvented, but any synaptic barriers which exist may still prevent the substances from reaching synaptic regions. By contrast, Skoglund (1961) has described the action of small doses of noradrenaline (about 1 μg/kg in cats) upon the discharge of spinal interneurones, and has reported that, in general, an enhanced excitability resulted. His animals were unanesthe-

tized, while those of Curtis, Phillis, and Watkins were under barbiturate anesthesia, and it would seem possible that this factor may again serve to explain the differences. This suggestion is the more attractive in that it is again a facilitatory effect which is abolished by the anesthesia.

In the experiments of McLennan (1961a), solutions of the catecholamines were also applied topically to the exposed spinal cord and the effect upon the knee-jerk reflex noted. In this investigation, the action of dopamine was found to be very much greater than that of noradrenaline, while adrenaline was ineffective. The effect observed was an inhibition of the reflex during the period of application, which could be prevented by the beta receptor-blocking agent dichloroisopropylnoradrenaline, but not by those drugs blocking alpha receptors. Very high concentrations (2.5 to 5 per cent solutions) were used, but the fact that dopamine was so much more effective than noradrenaline would appear to indicate an action other than one caused by vascular changes. Once again, however, this substance has been reported by Curtis (1962) not to affect Renshaw cells, interneurones, or motoneurones when applied iontophoretically; but McLennan (1962) did detect a small number of interneurones, activated through the reticulospinal pathways, whose discharge was enhanced by topically applied dopamine. All of these results cannot be interpreted more closely than to indicate that the catecholamines may influence neuronal excitability in the cord, but whether this action is a synaptic one is in no way proved and, indeed, the weight of evidence would appear to be against this view. For a further discussion of the possible role of dopamine as a synaptic transmitter, see page 98.

The effects of adrenaline upon higher functions of the central nervous system have been found, again, to vary with the dose and route of administration of the material. Larger doses, particularly if administered into the cerebrospinal fluid, tend to have depressant effects which are often preceded by a period of enhanced activity, while smaller doses are, in the main, excitatory only. However, Feldberg and Sherwood (1954a) have found that even small doses given into the lateral ventricles may produce a stuporous condition in an animal. They have suggested that when adrenaline enters the ventricular fluid depression occurs, and that excitation is observed only when it is present in the blood (Draskoci, Feldberg, and Haranath, 1960).

In 1904 Weber described the insensitivity to pain which followed upon the administration of adrenaline by lumbar puncture and which appeared to be selective in that reflex activity to other than painful stimuli was retained. This action has been confirmed by others (e.g., Bass, 1914), and Ivy, Goetzl, Harris, and Burrill (1944) were able to carry out surgical procedures in dogs after intracarotid or intravenous injection of adrenaline, during which period consciousness was apparently retained. These effects indicate a selective action of adrenaline upon certain neurones of the central nervous system, specifically those concerned with pain sensation, rather than the production of a generalized depression. However, again it is not clear whether the effects are exerted upon synaptic areas. These actions are believed to be exerted in the hypothalamus and the rostral part of the peri-aqueductal grey substance (Domer and Feldberg, 1960), which are areas normally containing large amounts of noradrenaline (Table V).

The existence of specific adrenergic mechanisms in the reticular formation has been postulated by Dell, Bonvallet, and Hugelin (1954) to explain both the EEG arousal and the facilitation of postural reflexes which are observed after adrenaline administration, and which can no longer be obtained after destruction of this area. It is to be noted that a desynchronized EEG is a feature also of an animal which has been rendered stuporous by the administration of adrenaline (Rothballer, 1959), and another example of the dissociation of EEG patterns and behavior is presented thereby. Ling and Foulks (1959) have confirmed the EEG activation by the intra-innominate administration of very small doses of adrenaline in chronically de-afferented cats which require no anesthesia and exhibit a stable synchronized resting pattern. In spite of this evidence suggestive of the existence of an adrenergic step in the ascending reticular activating pathway, there is still doubt as to whether the changes might not be due to local vascular effects even though they are clearly not related to the changes occurring in the main systemic circulation. Although this cannot be finally excluded as a possible explanation, it would seem that the balance of evidence is probably in favor of an adrenergic mechanism being involved (see the discussion by Dell, 1960).

There is essentially no evidence for the presence of adrenergic synapses among the invertebrates, and the catecholamines have not been found in animals other than annelids, insects, and cephalopods. It is, therefore, noteworthy that these substances are able to cause profound effects upon the organs of animals which do not contain them; thus, for example, adrenaline accelerates the heart beats of a number of crustacea (Florey and Florey, 1954) and exerts other actions in these animals as well. The inference again must be that receptor areas which are able to respond to these materials are relatively nonspecific, and do not require the physiological application of the substances for their development. In the light of this it is difficult to ascribe a synaptic function at any site to the catecholamines even in those species where they have been detected, for the demonstration of specific adrenergic nerve fibers is completely lacking.

In summary, it may be said that the evidence for the role of noradrenaline as the transmitter of postganglionic sympathetic activity in vertebrates is good, and that the localization of the material to certain areas of the brain is suggestive of its function there as a mediator of synaptic action. Nevertheless, this has not been directly proven, and no definitely ascribable adrenergic synapse has been detected either in the vertebrate central nervous system or throughout the invertebrate kingdom.

5-HYDROXYTRYPTAMINE

Unlike acetylcholine and noradrenaline, the amounts of 5-hydroxytryptamine (and of substance P and histamine, which will be considered in later sections) found in the brain are small by comparison with their concentrations in some other structures of the body. Nevertheless, 5-hydroxytryptamine has been the subject of intensive study, particularly in relation to the mode of action of its pharmacological antagonists upon the central nervous system, and many would accept the hypothesis that 5-hydroxytryptamine acts as a central synaptic transmitter in spite of the paucity of evidence directly bearing upon this point.

5-Hydroxytryptamine is present in the central nervous system in highest concentration in the hypothalamus as also is noradrenaline; and the enzyme systems responsible for its synthesis and destruction (DOPA decarboxylase and monamine oxidase) are also concentrated there (Table V). On this basis, in part, Brodie and Shore (1957) suggested that 5-hydroxytryptamine might be the transmitter substance characteristic of the central parasympathetic system, with noradrenaline occupying the corresponding role for the sympathetic. Their hypothesis is based also upon certain pharmacological facts. In 1953 Gaddum first demonstrated that an antagonism between 5-hydroxytryptamine and lysergic acid diethylamide (LSD) could be demonstrated which was in the nature of a competition for receptor sites between the two substances (Gaddum and Hameed, 1954). The psychogenic properties of LSD are well known, and, in addition, its administration produces marked central sympathetic activation which would be expected to occur if the central parasympathetic transmitter had been prevented from exerting its normal function. The other evidence adduced by Brodie and Shore is more difficult to assess, for at the time their hypothesis was put forward, the alkaloid reserpine was known to deplete endogenous stores of 5-hydroxytryptamine in the body but its similar action upon the catecholamines was unrecognized. Inasmuch as it is now known that not only is the 5-hydroxytryptamine of the brain rapidly liberated from its storage sites following reserpine treatment but also the same is true for noradrenaline (Muscholl and Vogt, 1958), the results obtained in such experiments, and in those in which treatment with reserpine and an inhibitor of monamine oxidase is combined, would be expected to show a multiplicity of effects which may be impossible to unravel.

Gaddum and Vogt (1956) have investigated the actions of LSD and of 5-hydroxytryptamine following injection into the cerebral ventricles and concluded that there is little evidence to suggest that the central actions of LSD can be correlated with interference with a normal tryptaminergic mechanism. There are thus considerable uncertainties in the available data; and although it seems unlikely that the localization of 5-hydroxytryptamine to certain areas of the brain is coincidental, its precise role there cannot be determined. It must also be pointed out that although LSD is both an hallucinogen and an antagonist of 5-hydroxytryptamine, some antagonists (e.g., 2-bromo-LSD) are not hallucinogenic (Cerletti and Rothlin, 1955), while some hallucinogens are not 5-hydroxytryptamine antagonists, of which the best examples are certain of the oxidation products of adrenaline.

The actions observed following intraventricular administration of 5-hydroxytryptamine vary with the dose, administration of smaller amounts being somewhat depressant and characterized by muscular weakness (Feldberg and Sherwood, 1954a), while much larger doses are definitely excitatory and may even lead to convulsions (Wooley, 1957). Although 5-hydroxytryptamine itself does not freely pass the blood-brain barrier, systemic administration of derivatives of it, which *in vitro* have been shown to possess similar actions, produces profound excitation of a number of areas, especially in the spinal cord. These observations have led Vane, Collier, Corne, Marley, and Bradley (1961) to conclude that tryptaminergic receptors are widely distributed in the central nervous system and that there is a physiological function for them. There are, in addition, a number of reports in the literature on the effects of 5-hydroxytryptamine upon spinal reflexes, which can be distinguished from the blood pressure changes accompanying the administration. Although the effects are somewhat variable, in general the material produces a transient potentiation of polysynaptic flexor reflexes and an inhibition of monosynaptic extensor action (Weidmann and Cerletti, 1957). The latter action, at least, is critically dependent upon the chemical structure of the substance administered, for if the hydroxyl group upon the indole nucleus is shifted from the five to the four position, the compounds exert a marked enhancing action upon extensor reflexes instead of the inhibition exhibited by 5-hydroxytryptamine and its congeners (Weidmann and Cerletti, 1960). An antagonism between 5-hydroxytryptamine and LSD was observed in all these situations.

Nevertheless, there remains grave doubt whether this substance exerts its effects directly upon neurones in these experiments. Not only does it penetrate with difficulty through the blood-brain barrier, but Curtis, Phillis, and Watkins (1961a) have failed to show that it can influence interneurones in the cord when applied to them iontophoretically, and the conclusion was drawn by these authors that 5-hydroxytryptamine was unlikely to function either as an excitatory or an inhibitory transmitter within the cord. As was the case for the catecholamines discussed in the previous section, there are unexplained discrepancies which urgently require elucidation: on the one hand, the marked effects which can be obtained by systemic administration of these materials or of pharmacological agents which influence their action, and on the other, the total lack of effect which is observed following their application to the near neighborhood of individual neurones. Were it not for the convincing results obtained with the iontophoretic method in the case of the certainly cholinergic Renshaw cells, one might be justified in suspecting a technical fault as explaining some of the discrepancies; but it would seem that this is unjustified. One can only state in summary that the evidence for tryptaminergic synapses within the spinal cord is indirect and somewhat uncertain.

Among the higher structures with which 5-hydroxytryptamine has been implicated is the lateral geniculate body. Evarts, Landau, Freygang, and Marshall (1955) demonstrated, and others have confirmed, that LSD blocks the synapse between the optic nerve and optic radiation fibers and there is evidence that the block is a competitive one with the normal excitatory transmitter in that situation (Bishop, Burke, and Hayhow, 1959). In view of the known antagonism between 5-hydroxytryptamine and LSD, it was a not unreasonable hypothesis that the former compound might be the transmitter in question, although it is to be noted that 5-hydroxytryptamine is apparently not present in the geniculate bodies (Table V). The suggestion has, however, apparently been ruled out by the results of Curtis and Davis (1961, 1962), who applied 5-hydroxytryptamine iontophoretically to single neurones of the lateral geniculate bodies and have found that orthodromic action potentials are blocked by the application, although antidromic stimulation or glutamate activation of the cells was uninfluenced. Other agents also depressed the response; among these were tryptamine, LSD, dopamine, noradrenaline, adrenaline, and 2-bromo-LSD, in decreasing order of potency. Thus, there is a parallelism between the actions of 5-hydroxytryptamine and LSD in this case rather than an antagonism, and this appears to be a general feature of central nervous system effects (see Page, 1958). Curtis and Davis concluded that since the antidromic response of the cells was unaffected, 5-hydroxytryptamine and the other substances were not reacting with inhibitory synapses, and that the most probable explanation of their results was an interaction with the excitatory receptor areas resulting in a blocking of their reactivity to the normal transmitter. This conclusion is in accord with

the findings of Bishop, Burke, and Hayhow (1959), who showed that repetitive presynaptic stimulation would overcome an LSD block, again indicating a competitive type of interaction. Thus, although 5-hydroxytryptamine itself appears not to be the normal transmitter of these synapses, it is likely that some compound, structurally similar, is involved. K. Krnjević and J. W. Phillis (Personal Communication) have also found that 5-hydroxytryptamine depresses the synaptic activation of neurones of the cerebral cortex, but in this case glutamate activation was altered as well, so that a different mechanism, presumably involving conductance changes in the membrane, would seem to be involved here. Again there is no indication of a function for 5-hydroxytryptamine as a transmitter of synaptic events. Curtis and Koizumi (1961) failed to detect any cells in the brain stem which were either excited or inhibited by 5-hydroxytryptamine.

In autonomic ganglia a situation reminiscent of that described above for the effects of the catecholamines exists. Trendelenberg (1957) found that the responses of the superior cervical ganglion were potentiated by the intra-arterial injection of small amounts of the substance, while Marrazzi (1953) described inhibition in the ciliary ganglion following considerably larger amounts. Although it seems probable that the effect described by Trendelenberg is one upon the neurones themselves, there is no indication that 5-hydroxytryptamine is directly involved in the transmission process. Not only does the substance appear not to be present in ganglia, and consequently is not released from them upon stimulation (Gertner, Paasonen, and Giarman, 1957); LSD furthermore has only a small depressing effect upon the transmission process (Broghammer, Takagi, and Schaefer, 1957). Whether in fact some mechanism similar to that mediated by an adrenergic compound in ganglia exists with a tryptaminergic basis is unknown, but may be presumed unlikely.

Among invertebrates, 5-hydroxytryptamine or compounds having similar biological properties (since again in most cases the identification has been made on the basis of pharmacological and not chemical tests) are fairly widespread. 5-Hydroxytryptamine certainly exists in the nervous systems of some mollusks, since it has been demonstrated there by both biological (Florey and Florey, 1954; Welsh, 1957) and chemical assay (Welsh and Moorehead, 1959). Florey and Florey (1954) also reported the presence in crustacean nervous tissue of a substance biologically identified as 5-hydroxytryptamine, but which Carlisle (1956 and Personal Communication) has shown probably to be 5,6-dihydroxytryptamine and to exist also in the tissue in what is presumably a precursor form. This agent occurs in the pericardial organs, which are essentially nerve endings lying free in the blood and into which the active material is secreted by excitation of the axons. This in turn causes cardiac acceleration in all decapod crustacea except *Maia squinado,* in which arrest of the heart is brought about (Alexandrowicz and Carlisle, 1953). 5-Hydroxytryptamine, and therefore perhaps the dihydroxy form as well, also causes the excitation of skeletal muscle of crayfish (Florey, 1954a), apparently through its ability to excite sensory cells, which results in a reflex contraction of the muscle. van der Kloot (1960) has extracted a material which appears in a perfusion fluid during stimulation of motor axons in crayfish and which causes rapid and reversible muscle contraction when injected. He has called the material "Factor S" and has produced some evidence that it may be a one-substituted nicotinamide derivative, although the possibility of its having an indole structure cannot be excluded. A further study of the interrelationships of these compounds should be of considerable interest.

The role of 5-hydroxytryptamine in mollusks is unknown, although very large amounts are found in some tissues; e.g., 760 μg/g in the posterior salivary glands of *Eledone moschata* (Erspamer, 1954). It has an effect upon the hearts of these animals mimicking the action of the cardio-accelerator nerves; but whether this is a physiological function or even whether 5-hydroxytryptamine is in fact released upon stimulation of the appropriate axons has not been ascertained. It is of interest that Carlisle (1962) has shown the 5,6-dihydroxytryptamine of crustacea to be very much more active than the 5-hydroxy derivative, and therefore the large concentrations of 5-hydroxytryptamine such as have been reported in *Eledone* may not be real, inasmuch as again the identification has been on the basis of biological and not chemical tests.

In the anterior retractor muscle of the byssus of *Mytilus edulis,* the application of 5-hydroxytryptamine abolishes the tonic contraction which is a feature of the tissue without interfering with its normal phasic response to nerve stimulation or to the application of acetylcholine (Hoyle and Lowy, 1956; Twarog, 1960). Since the muscle contains 5-hydroxytryptamine (determined by biological assay) and monoamine oxidase, the supposition is that this may be a physiologically important process in which 5-hydroxytryptamine plays a role as a "relaxing factor," possibly released *in vivo* by nerve stimulation.

In summary, it may be said that although 5-hydroxytryptamine, or a compound similar to it, has a wide distribution in nervous and other tissues throughout the animal kingdom, and has been shown in a number of instances to mimic the effects of nerve stimulation, there is no single case in which it can be ascribed a role as a transmitter, or among invertebrates, a neurohumoral role. That it does subserve such functions appears most likely, but definite proof for this thesis is lacking.

SUBSTANCE P AND THE "SENSORY TRANSMITTER"

Substance P, originally described by von Euler and Gaddum (1931) as an agent extractable from the gut and active in promoting smooth muscle contraction, is present in the nervous system with a distribution resembling those of noradrenaline and of 5-hydroxytryptamine, but being in addition high in the dorsal columns of the cord (Table V). The material has recently been prepared in a highly purified form (Franz, Boissonnas, and Stürmer, 1961) and is a polypeptide small enough to penetrate cellophane and collodion membranes (von Euler, 1936). It can be differentiated by pharmacological and chemical tests from other substances present in the body which stimulate smooth muscle and, assuming a molecular weight for it of not less than 1,000, it is many times more active in this respect, molecule for molecule, than is acetylcholine. Substance P has never been reported to occur in animals other than the vertebrates.

Substance P is a potent stimulator of smooth muscle, especially of the small intestine, which is also its region of highest concentration in the body. Its actions there are not blocked by atropine or ganglionic-blocking agents and it therefore probably acts directly on the muscle cells, although some indication of a neurotropic component of the response has been reported by Blair and Clark (1956).

There is no evidence either to support or disprove the suggestion that it is released upon nerve stimulation and its role in the normal function of the intestine, while very probable, is not well defined.

Substance P exhibits effects upon nervous structures, but these are not striking. Its intra-arterial administration in low dose has been reported to enhance and in higher doses to depress the response of the superior cervical ganglion both to electrical and to acetylcholine stimulation (Beleslin, Radmanović, and Varagić, 1960), and its action is thus reminiscent of other materials described above. In the central nervous system its intraventricular admistration (von Euler and Pernow, 1956) led to autonomic changes which are again very like those obtained following administration of a variety of other agents (Feldberg and Sherwood, 1954a); and in both of these situations it seems highly unlikely that the effects obtained are in any way to be specifically associated with substance P. The central effects after systemic administration have been investigated by Zetler (1956), who demonstrated that "sedation" and an antagonism to certain central-stimulating agents occurred while at the same time the animals exhibited an hyperalgesia and the action of morphine was prevented. Lechner and Lembeck (1958) demonstrated that the material gave rise to an arousal response in both cortex and hippocampus, and suggested that substance P in this case was acting directly to excite non-cholinergic neurones in the ascending reticular-activating system. Pointing out that the administration of a transmitter of inhibitory neurones would be expected to result in depression, and administration of a sensory transmitter, hyperalgesia, Zetler (1960) has proposed that substance P fulfills both these roles in different areas of the central nervous system. It is, however, entirely obvious that there is almost no direct evidence based on the criteria given earlier which would substantiate such a claim, although, on the other hand, there is none which can directly confute it.

It should be noted in passing that recent evidence suggests that the neurologically active material may not be the same as the smooth muscle-stimulating polypeptide (Bonta, Wijmenga, and Hohensee, 1961). Zetler (1961) has also shown that the "substance P" (defined in terms of a smooth muscle effect), prepared from brain, contains several pharmacologically active materials.

Another area in which interest in the possible involvement of substance P as a synaptic transmitter has been considerable is at the central synapses of primary sensory neurones; the question here is whether substance P can be identified with the "sensory transmitter." One of the principal proponents of this hypothesis has been Lembeck (1953), who has pointed out that in the central nervous system substance P is present in high concentration in the dorsal white columns of the spinal cord and in the posterior roots; and Amin, Crawford, and Gaddum (1954) reported also its presence in comparatively large amounts in the nuclei cuneatus et gracilis. Inouye and Kataoka (1062) have localized it to an ultracentrifugal fraction containing synaptic vesicles and have confirmed its higher concentration in the posterior half of the cord. Its possible connection with primary sensory synaptic transmission therefore seems a not unreasonable proposition.

Direct evidence for the suggestion has, however, not been forthcoming and therefore a definitive answer to the problem cannot be given. Nevertheless, a considerable amount of work has been carried out, and it is pertinent to undertake a discussion of this matter here.

In 1935 Dale enunciated the thesis, which has been widely accepted, that if a neurone releases a given substance at one branch of its axon which has a function as a synaptic transmitter, then the same substance will be released at the synapses formed by all other branches of the axon. Experimental confirmation of this principle has been achieved in only one instance, namely at the synapses between motor axon collaterals and the Renshaw cells of the anterior horn of the cord, which synapses are beyond reasonable doubt cholinergic, as are the motor end-plates which form the other principal termination of these axons. Dale's hypothesis assumes a special significance in the case of the primary sensory neurones which are bipolar in nature, with one branch peripherally directed and the other forming central connections in the cord or medulla.

Stricker (1876) appears to have been the first to observe the vasodilatation produced peripherally when the distal end of sectioned posterior roots were stimulated, and although controversy followed his description, it is now accepted as a real phenomenon and has retained the name "antidromic vasodilatation," which Bayliss (1901) gave to it. Bayliss was also able to satisfy himself that the axons giving rise to the dilatation were indistinguishable from ordinary sensory fibers. Langley (1923), taking note of the long latency between stimulation and response which Bayliss had also described, felt that the release of a substance from the peripheral endings of the fibers was the cause of the dilatation, on the grounds that a diffusional delay would explain the long latency of the response. These observations have been repeatedly confirmed. On the assumption that the sensory nerve fibers are in fact identical to those bringing about the dilatation, then it was felt that the substance released peripherally and centrally might be identical, i.e., that the centrally acting sensory synaptic transmitter and the vasodilator material released upon antidromic stimulation would be the same, this being a logical application of Dale's principle. Any material which when administered into an area of the skin produced there a capillary dilatation might thus be regarded as a possible candidate for the synaptic agent. Extensive investigative work has been carried out on the basis of this premise.

Before describing these investigations however, it must be mentioned that there is still some doubt concerning the identification of the vasodilator with the sensory fibers. Cajal (1890) and von Lenhossék (1890) have described the existence (in the chick) of efferent axons in the posterior roots arising from cells in the posterior portion of the anterior horns of the cord, and this finding has been extended to other vertebrates. The possibility exists, therefore, that these are the axons which give rise to the dilatation and that the reaction is not, in fact, an antidromic one. This question is still unsettled.

Doubt also surrounds the nature of the material released upon stimulation of the posterior roots, whether it is released from sensory or from other fibers. It has been remarked above that acetylcholine is very effective in stimulating many types of sensory endings and the same is true in this case. Armin and Grant (1953) have demonstrated the pronounced vasodilator action of small doses of acetylcholine administered intra-arterially into the rabbit's ear, and this result has been confirmed by many others. Nevertheless, it has been argued by Holton and Perry (1951) that acetylcholine cannot be the substance liberated physiologically and giving rise to the reaction, inasmuch as the response to injected acetylcholine can be blocked by atropine while

the dilatation following nerve stimulation is unaffected thereby. Antidromic vasodilatation is also unaffected by large doses of hemicholinium #3 (H. McLennan and C. R. Muirhead, Unpublished Observations). Sensory roots have been reported to contain little or no acetylcholine (Loewi and Hellauer, 1938; MacIntosh, 1941); however, Wybauw (1936) was able to detect its liberation peripherally during antidromic vasodilatation and further stated that although atropine did not block the normal response, it did reduce the potentiated dilatation observed by him in the presence of eserine. Wybauw's conclusion was that the phenomenon was cholinergic in nature, and although this is not now widely accepted, the matter cannot be entirely regarded as settled. It must also not be forgotten that the effects of injected acetylcholine do not always perfectly imitate the response to nerve stimulation, even in certainly cholinergic sites, and the effects of pharmacological agents upon the two types of stimulation are also not invariably parallel. Reference to this matter has been made earlier.

There are a considerable number of other compounds which, when administered intra-arterially into a rabbit's ear, give rise to a dilatation of the capillaries. Of this number, two will be discussed here as being the most likely to be be related to antidromic vasodilatation and to be worthy of comparison with the actions of extracts prepared from central nervous system tissue. These are substance P and adenosine triphosphate (ATP). It cannot be denied that these are both potent vasodilators, and there are no known pharmacological agents which prevent their action.

Lembeck (1953) has been the principal proponent of the importance of substance P in this connection, and has stressed the fact that it is present in posterior roots in much greater amount than in anterior roots, and has noted also its distribution throughout the course of the primary sensory neurones. He has concluded that this material might be the sensory transmitter of the central synapses. The auricular nerve of the rabbit, stimulation of which gives rise to dilatation in the ear, contains substance P apparently only in the sensory fibers and this gradually disappears following section of the nerve trunk (Andrews and Holton, 1958; Holton, 1959b). Umrath (1953) has also found that the substance P of sensory fibers falls after they are cut off from their cell bodies; but, unlike Lembeck, he does not consider that it can be the sensory transmitter itself, nor that it is the vasodilator material found in nerve and brain. Rather, he is of the opinion (Umrath, 1961) that it is the precursor of the active material, and he accepts the concept that the vasodilator and central sensory transmitter are the same. Holton and Perry (1951) have also claimed that substance P cannot be the material present in tissue extracts, for the latter is insoluble in acetone and labile in hot acid solution and this is not true for the polypeptide. Hellauer (1953) agrees that substance P and the vasodilator material extracted from nervous tissue are different, but the chemical data given by him for substance P are at variance with those obtained by others (Pernow, 1955).

ATP has been proposed as the agent of antidromic vasodilatation largely through the work of Holton and her associates. They have shown that ATP is a potent capillary vasodilator (Holton and Holton, 1954); that although it is present in roughly equal concentrations in both sensory and motor roots, it rapidly disappears from the latter after excision; and, most importantly, that it is released upon antidromic stimulation of the auricular nerve in rabbits (Holton, 1959a). In spite of this evidence, it seems *a priori* rather improbable that ATP itself would function as a synaptic transmitter in view of its widespread distribution and its general role in cellular metabolism. The work of Blaschko, Born, D'Iorio, and Eade (1956) and of Schümann (1958), who have demonstrated a probable binding of catecholamines by ATP in the adrenal medulla and in sympathetic nerves respectively, may provide an explanation of its liberation upon sensory nerve stimulation, i.e., that in this case it also binds or is associated with the transmitter and is released with it upon activation of the fibers. In this case it would be expected, as Holton (1959a) has pointed out, that it could have a physiological role as a vasodilator, although not acting centrally as a mediator of synaptic events.

The connection either of ATP or substance P with the vasodilator material which can be extracted from nervous tissue is not clear. Hellauer and Umrath (1948) were the first to make such extracts and to test them by intradermal injection into rabbits' ears. They showed that the vasodilatation produced was enhanced if the ear was previously denervated, and concluded therefrom that the sensory transmitter was involved, arguing from Dale's principle and from analogy with the heightened sensitivity to the normal transmitter which is observed following denervation in other situations. Florey and McLennan (1955c) confirmed this observation and showed also that the response to ATP was not potentiated by denervation, from which the conclusion can be drawn that not all of the activity of the extracts can be due to ATP. Furthermore, H. McLennan and C. R. Muirhead (Unpublished Observations) have failed to find a positive correlation between the vasodilator activity of various regions of the central nervous system and their content of ATP, although their results in general agreed with those of Harris and Holton (1953) for the distribution of vasodilator material in the brain (Table V). On the other hand, the extracts prepared by Holton and Holton (1954) by a different method did contain ATP apparently in amounts sufficiently to account fully for their dilator action, and it is evident that here again there is an area of discrepancy which is unsolved. It would seem safe to conclude that the vasodilator activity of a crude extract of brain is due in part to its content of substance P, in part to ATP, and in part to an unidentified material.

What then is the relationship between the vasodilator material and the sensory transmitter? If Dale's principle holds true, and if it is in fact the antidromic excitation of sensory fibers in the posterior roots which is responsible for the dilatation following stimulation, then the two may be expected to be identical. There is no known pharmacology of primary sensory synapses, so that no information (other than of a negative nature) can be obtained from this source. Both the distribution of ATP and its other known functions combine to make it an unlikely candidate as a transmitter agent, although it may well be released as a part of the general transmission process. Furthermore, its actions upon nervous tissue are not striking, and are manifest principally as a reduction of acetylcholine-induced effects (Robinson and Hughes, 1951). Substance P has in its favor the fact that its distribution agrees with that of the primary sensory neurones, but chemically it seems not to be identical with the dilator substance. Umrath's suggestion that it may be a precursor both of dilator and of the sensory transmitter may be a way out of this difficulty, but has little evidence to support it. The actual identity of the transmitter active at the central synapses must be regarded as still unknown.

In this context it may be as well to discuss briefly the possible role of histamine as a central synaptic transmitter. It too has been proposed as the mediator of antidromic vaso-dilatation. The substance is present in fair amount in the posterior roots (Kwiatowski, 1943) and its administration into the rabbit's ear has been reported occasionally to produce marked dilatation (Holton and Perry, 1951), although McLennan and Muirhead observed only constriction following even small doses. The effect of administered histamine, but not that of nerve stimulation, can be blocked by antihistamine drugs, and the weight of evidence against this substance being involved physiologically is considerable (Holton and Perry, 1951). In autonomic ganglia it has been reported that histamine is able to enhance the transmission process (Trendelenberg, 1957). Within the central nervous system its only region of striking concentration is, once more, the hypothalamus (Table V). On the basis of these distributions it has been suggested as a possible modulator of general sympathetic activity, but if this is so, it seems unlikely to be involved primarily at synapses. There is no evidence in favor of the concept that histamine in any situation acts as a synaptic transmitter substance.

FACTOR I AND THE "INHIBITORY TRANSMITTER"

As is true of the sensory transmitter, the mediator of inhibitory synapses in the central nervous system of vertebrates is chemically unidentified. Nevertheless, there is clear evidence, which has been amply discussed in Chapters 4 and 5, that such synapses exist and that the action of their characteristic transmitter is to cause specific permeability changes in the subsynaptic areas which are qualitatively different from those occuring at excitatory sites. A further valuable tool in the study of these mechanisms is the pharmacological fact that inhibitory synapses are competitively and specifically blocked by low doses of strychnine (Bradley, Easton, and Eccles, 1953; Curtis, 1959). Any substance which is postulated as having an action at inhibitory synapses must therefore be shown to have its effect similarly blocked by subconvulsive doses of strychnine.

Florey (1953) in a preliminary note and later in more detail (Florey, 1954b) first described the inhibitory action of extracts of vertebrate brain upon the stretch receptor neurones and other organs of crayfish, and demonstrated also their anti-acetylcholine effect upon mammalian smooth muscle. The material was dialyzable and water soluble, stable in hot neutral solution and insoluble in organic liquids. The most purified preparations which have been made do not show a ninhydrin reaction (Florey, 1954b; McLennan, 1960a). The crayfish stretch receptor neurone has continued to be the most useful test object for the routine assay of this inhibitory material (which Florey [1954b] named Factor I), although it is now clear that the receptor areas upon the stretch receptor neurones react with a large number of compounds (Edwards and Kuffler, 1959; McGeer, McGeer, and McLennan, 1961).

The evidence which has led to the suggestion that Factor I might contain the vertebrate inhibitory transmitter may be summarized as follows:

(1) It occurs exclusively in tissues of the central nervous system and appears in an exudate from these tissues (Florey and McLennan, 1955a).

(2) It is destroyed by an enzyme present in brain (Florey, 1954b).

(3) It inhibits monosynaptic reflex action in the spinal cord when topically applied to the exposed tissue, and this inhibition is completely prevented by a small dose of strychnine (Florey and McLennan, 1955b).

(4) Extensor motoneurones of the spinal cord exhibit an hyperpolarization with an associated reduction in amplitude of both EPSP's and IPSP's under the influence of Factor I (McLennan, 1960b, 1961b). These changes are to be expected following the exogenous application of the inhibitory transmitter (Curtis, Phillis, and Watkins, 1959).

(5) The sensory synapses in the nucleus gracilis are inhibited by Factor I (Honour and McLennan, 1960).

Comparison of this list with that given in Chapter 3 indicates that there was some reasonable ground for the hypothesis that the active ingredient of the extracts exerted its effect upon neuronal inhibitory synapses. It was also noted that in a number of instances the effects of applied acetylcholine and of Factor I were related in that some acetylcholine actions were blocked by Factor I and others imitated by it. Antagonistic actions have been reported in sympathetic ganglia (except the superior cervical) (Florey and McLennan, 1955a); upon mammalian intestine (Florey and McLennan, 1959), sea urchin esophagus (Florey and McLennan, 1959), squid rectum (Florey, 1956), and the intestine and stretch receptor neurones of crayfish (Florey, 1954b). Identical effects were observed upon the hypoglossal nucleus (Florey and McLennan, 1955b) and the hearts of frogs (Romanowski, Lenartowicz, and Janczarski, 1957) and cephalopods (Florey, 1956). Although, as we have seen, acetylcholine affects many structures, some of which do not receive a cholinergic innervation, this relationship to the actions of Factor I, both in regard to the possible structure of the active ingredient of the latter and to its likely site of action, is of interest and possible importance. It is to be noted that Factor I does not interfere with the processes of mammalian neuromuscular transmission (Florey and McLennan, 1955a), so that its relationship to acetylcholine is not an invariable finding.

The most useful piece of evidence supporting the possible transmitter role of Factor I is its ability to inhibit the knee-jerk reflex and the prevention of this process by strychnine (Figure 6.4). This may be related to the hyperpolarization of the cells involved, which is brought about by the application of the material to the exposed spinal cord. However, all motoneurones receive an inhibitory synaptic supply, and yet gross measurement of the effect of Factor I upon flexor reflexes (Florey

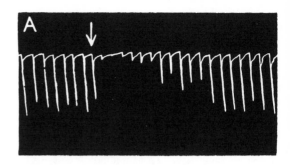

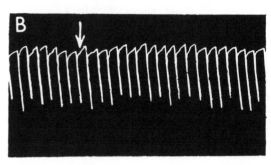

Figure 6.4. The effect upon the knee jerk reflex of the topical application (at the arrows) of a solution of Factor I to the exposed cat's spinal cord (*A*) before and (*B*) 5 minutes after the intravenous administration of 0.08 mg./kg. strychnine. (From Florey and McLennan, 1955b, by permission of the Journal of Physiology.)

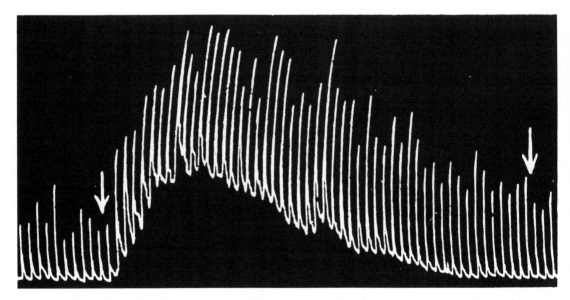

Figure 6.5. The effect upon a flexor reflex of the topical application of Factor I to the spinal cord in the cat. Note both that the strength of the reflex contraction is enhanced and that there is an increase in the tone of the muscles, indicated by the raised baseline. The solution was applied at the first and washed off at the second arrow. (From Florey and McLennan, 1955b, by permission of the Journal of Physiology.)

and McLennan, 1955b) yielded a different result from that observed in the monosynaptic pathways. In these cases the reflex was found to be enhanced by the application of the material to the cord, often with a concomitant increase in the tone of the muscles involved (Figure 6.5). If it is true that the Factor is effective at inhibitory synapses, this observation is difficult to explain. A possible way out could be provided if Factor I, rather than acting directly upon inhibitory motoneuronal synapses, influenced instead the discharge of the interneuronal pool in the cord such as to lead to the excitation of these cells. Extensor motoneurones receiving intense monosynaptic Ia afferent activation during elicitation of the knee-jerk reflex might be expected to respond to interneuronal excitation by an inhibition resulting from the firing of those inhibitory interneurones which make synaptic contact with them (see Table I). This might not be the case when a polysynaptic flexor reflex was

evoked. In this latter instance, activation of the interneuronal pool could conceivably reinforce the excitation of the motoneurones.

Although this question of whether Factor I acts directly upon motoneurones and therefore might contain the inhibitory transmitter or only indirectly through one or more interneurones is of fundamental interest, it cannot be answered at present. The iontophoretic techniques employed by Curtis and his colleagues, to which reference has been made repeatedly above, cannot be employed with unequivocal results unless the identification of the active ingredient is known, and this has so far not been achieved. Some slight pieces of information, however, may bear out the suggestion as at least a partial explanation of some of the actions of Factor I. These results are taken from unpublished experiments made by McLennan.

If a small recording electrode is placed in the intermediate nucleus of Cajal in the spinal

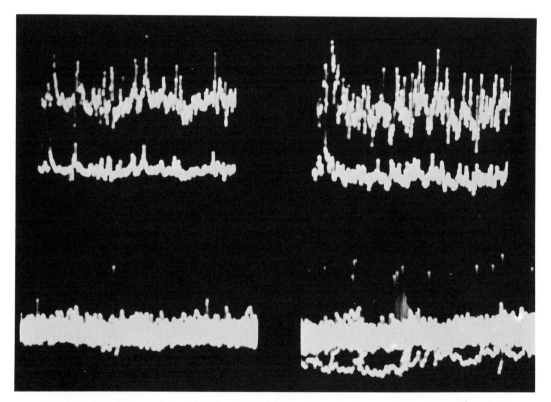

Figure 6.6. Above: records of the discharges of cells in the intermediate nucleus of Cajal of the spinal cord of the cat, in response to just maximal stimulation of the medial gastrocnemius nerve. The upper traces are shown at 2½ times the amplification of the lower. Duration of the sweeps: 200 msec. Below: spontaneous discharges of another intermediate nucleus cell. Approximately 10 sweeps are superimposed. Duration of sweeps: 50 msec. In each case, the left hand records are controls and the right 20 sec. after the application of Factor I solution to the exposed dorsum of the cord. The enhancement of both evoked and spontaneous discharge is evident. (Unpublished results of H. McLennan.)

cord and Factor I solution applied topically to the tissue, an enhanced discharge of the interneuronal pool, whether spontaneous or in response to stimulation of a peripheral nerve trunk, is sometimes observed, although this is not invariably the case and not all neurones whose actions are recorded by the electrode are affected (Figure 6.6). Concomitantly, the amplitude of the monosynaptic reflex response of the motoneurones is reduced. It has not so far been possible to identify the interneurones involved in this enhanced discharge, but the results are consistent with the hypothesis given above. It is also uncertain whether this action is of sufficiently great intensity likely to be able to account for the very marked reflex inhibition which is observed to occur. The possibility that more than one site of action of a crude mixture, which a Factor I extract is, is involved must always be considered. It may be remarked also that the cells of the hypoglossal nucleus appear directly to be excited by Factor I (Florey and McLennan, 1955b).

Another instance of the apparent relationship of acetylcholine to Factor I, which has been mentioned earlier, is also found in the spinal cord. The cholinergically innervated Renshaw cells are markedly inhibited by the topical application of the Factor (Figure 6.7) and, therefore, they cannot be involved in the production of the reflex inhibition. This observation also reveals that mammalian neurones can be inhibited directly by Factor I, and therefore it must not be thought that all its actions are excitatory. Inhibition of other neurones has been found upon occasions elsewhere in the cord, but under circumstances in which it has not been possible to rule out the alternative explanation that they were due secondarily to excitation elsewhere. This is perhaps less likely in the case of the Renshaw cells, although supraspinal control of their activity has been demonstrated (Haase and

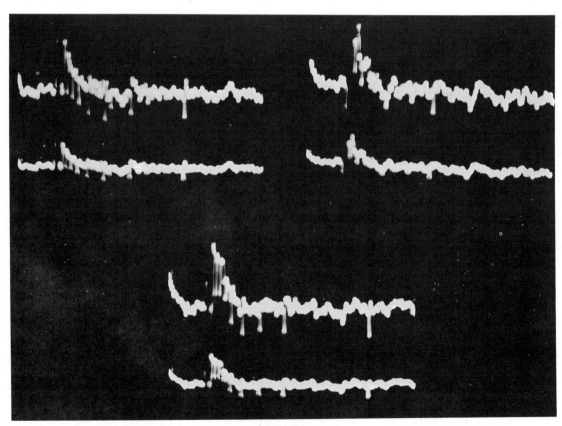

Figure 6.7. Records of the discharge of a Renshaw cell in the seventh lumbar segment of the cat's spinal cord. Upper left, control; right, 18 sec. after the topical application of Factor I to the exposed cord; below, after washing away the Factor I. Except for the first three discharges, the characteristic discharge pattern of the cell has been largely abolished by the application. Duration of sweeps: 200 msec. The upper trace in each case is at twice the amplification of the lower. (Unpublished results of H. McLennan.)

van den Meulen, 1961). There is no further information available on these questions at the present time.

In the case of the stretch receptor neurones of the crayfish, the action of Factor I must also be exerted directly upon the cells. Here, too, there are indications that the active material responsible for the abolition of the discharge acts by mimicking the stimulation of the inhibitory synapses impinging upon the cell, and the inhibition is to a very great extent prevented by picrotoxin (Florey, 1954b, 1957; McGeer, McGeer, and McLennan, 1961), which in these animals replaces strychnine as the agent blocking the inhibitory synapses. Factor I is derived from mammalian sources, but similar extracts can be prepared from invertebrate nervous tissue which also are active upon the stretch receptor neurone. To differentiate these extracts, Florey (1960a) named the active material from crustacean nerve "Substance I."

Attempts to identify the constituents of Factor I extracts have depended to a very large extent upon the sensitivity and ease of use of the crayfish neurone as a test object, although any compound is active which has an acidic and a basic functional group that can be oriented in such a way that they are approximately 4 Å apart and are sterically unhindered (McGeer, McGeer, and McLennan, 1961). Using this biological test as an assay method, Bazemore, Elliott, and Florey (1957) reported that extracts with Factor I activity contained gamma-aminobutyric acid (GABA), which is a potent inhibitor of the stretch receptor neurone discharge. Bazemore, Elliott, and Florey believed that all of the Factor I activity of brain could be accounted for in terms of GABA, but this now seems unlikely.

Although GABA apparently mimics the action of Factor I upon the crayfish neurone, it fails to do so in a number of other situations. In particular the topical application of this material to the spinal cord, even in high concentration, is without effect upon the knee-jerk reflex (McLennan, 1957b; Honour and McLennan, 1960) and it is similarly without influence upon the transmission process through the inferior mesenteric ganglion (Honour and McLennan, 1960; Matthews and Roberts, 1961). We will return to a more detailed consideration of some of the actions of GABA in a later section. It may be said here, however, that there is excellent evidence to show that it does not act in vertebrates as a transmitter substance released at inhibitory synapses.

The same is true also of two other materials which have been described in brain, gamma-aminobutyrylcholine and beta-hydroxy-gamma-aminobutyric acid. The existence of the first of these has been reported by Kuriaki, Yakushiji, Noro, Shimizu, and Saji (1958), and its anti-acetylcholine properties described by these authors and by Asano, Noro, and Kuriaki (1960). Its presence in brain was confirmed by Kewitz (1959). The most striking action of gamma-aminobutyrylcholine was reported by Takahashi, Nagashima, and Koshino (1958), who described its inhibitory effect upon cortical potentials evoked both directly and by stimulation of appropriate afferent pathways. This blocking effect is manifested also by GABA (Purpura, Girado, Smith, Callan, and Grundfest, 1959) and by Factor I (Honour and McLennan, 1960), but the choline ester was said to be 1000 times more potent. This action has not been confirmed by others (Purpura, 1960; Honour and McLennan, 1960), and the ester has no action upon individual neurones other than can be attributed to traces of GABA resulting from its hydrolysis (Curtis and Watkins, 1960). It seems most unlikely to possess a role as an inhibitory transmitter.

The presence of beta-hydroxy-gamma-aminobutyric acid in brain has been claimed by Hayashi (1959) and by Ohara, Sano, Koizumi, and Nishinuma (1959), although this could not be confirmed by C. Mitoma, S. Lindstedt, and J. J. Pisano (Personal Communication). Although Hayashi has reported that this material is very much more active than GABA in the prevention of electrically induced seizures in dogs, no indication of its greater potency than, or qualitative difference from, GABA in other situations has been found. Indeed, it has usually been found to be somewhat less active than GABA when comparisons have been made (McLennan, 1957b; Purpura, Girado, Smith, Callan, and Grundfest, 1959; Curtis and Watkins, 1960; Rech and Domino, 1960; McGeer, McGeer, and McLennan, 1961).

Although the crude brain extracts as routinely prepared for Factor I will almost certainly contain at least some GABA, it is evident from what has been said above that this material and its congeners cannot account for all of the actions of the extracts. One attempt to fractionate the extracts yielded two active components, both of which showed the full biological range exhibited by the crude material, and one had a specific activity on the crayfish neurone considerably greater than that of GABA (McLennan, 1960a). Neither appeared to contain a ninhydrin-reacting compound, and one gave evidence of being cationic, but further characterization was not achieved. From the studies of McGeer, McGeer, and McLennan (1961), two other materials appeared worthy of further study. One, 4-imidazoleacetic acid, had, on the average, 1.5 times the activity of GABA; but little further work has been devoted to it as yet, in spite of the fact that upon the crayfish it more closely resembled Factor I than did any other substance. Its production in the brain from histamine has been demonstrated (White, 1960).

The other compound, which in the hands of McGeer, McGeer, and McLennan showed a very much greater activity than GABA, was dopamine.* This material has a striking inhibitory effect upon the knee-jerk reflex when topically applied to the spinal cord (McLennan, 1961a), which effect, like that produced by Factor I, is abolished by strychnine and by the "beta" adrenergic-blocking agent dichloroisopropylnoradrenaline. The physiological inhibitory pathway impinging upon spinal motoneurones from the bulbar reticular formation is also blocked by dichloroisopropylnoradrenaline, and its effect cannot be detected in an animal treated with reserpine, which depletes the endogenous stores of all the catecholamines (Carlsson, 1959). It was therefore suggested not only that the presence of dopamine might explain certain of the biological effects of Factor I, but that this substance might be the transmitter of inhibitory synapses.

This latter suggestion has not been borne out by more detailed analysis. Curtis (1962) has failed to find that dopamine affects spinal moto- or interneurones following iontophoretic application; on the other hand, McLennan (1962) has been able to show that a few interneurones associated specifically with the reticulospinal pathway are excited by the substance topically applied to the cord. There are neurones, however, which are certainly inhibited by the iontophoretic application of dopamine. This has been demonstrated by J. W. Phillis and K. Krnjević (Personal Com-

*The finding that the catecholamines exhibited inhibitory properties is at variance with the results obtained earlier by Elliott and Florey (1956). It is now apparent that this discrepancy is probably due to species variation between crayfish, the *Orconectes sp.* used by Elliott and Florey being entirely unaffected by any of the catecholamines (McLennan and Hagen, 1962).

munication) for cells of the cerebral cortex, although these authors have also found that it is considerably weaker than GABA in this respect. It is therefore improbable that dopamine can be the inhibitory transmitter, although it does have actions upon neurones that are not shared by noradrenaline. What the connection between the high concentrations of dopamine in the telencephalic basal ganglia (see Table V) and the normal function of these structures may be is uncertain, but it may be presumed in the light of the above discussion that it is of physiological significance. Its possible involvement in basal ganglial disorders is also of great interest, especially in view of the pronounced extrapyramidal reactions which are provoked by some of the adrenergic-blocking agents and by reserpine.

It seems, on the whole, rather unlikely that all of the actions of Factor I extracts can be explained even by the combined effects of GABA and dopamine, especially in view of the fact that the latter requires the application of very high concentrations to the cord in order to elicit an effect, while GABA is entirely inactive. If Factor I does contain an inhibitory synaptic transmitter, it remains to be identified. There is some evidence to suggest, as we have seen, that a substance acting directly to inhibit motoneurones is present in the extracts which may yet prove to be that agent.

Although not demonstrable following topical application to the cord, GABA and its congeners do have effects upon spinal (and other) neurones. Curtis and Watkins (1960) have investigated a large number of substances and have shown that beta-alanine and GABA in particular were strongly depressant following iontophoretic application. The depression is characterized as follows (Curtis, Phillis, and Watkins, 1959): "The resting potential of motoneurones was not altered, but the membrane became less excitable when tested by electrical pulses and by orthodromically or antidromically evoked depolarizations that usually produce spike potentials. Further, not only excitatory but also IPSP's were diminished or even abolished and these effects of GABA and beta-alanine were not blocked by strychnine." These actions, it will be noted, differ from those described as characteristic of the action of the inhibitory transmitter (see p. 93) and from what is observed following application of Factor I, and may be explained not as a specific effect upon inhibitory synapses but as a generalized decrease in membrane permeability such that the whole neuronal soma is less excitable both to synaptic and to direct electrical stimulation (see also Bindman, Lippold, and Redfearn, 1962). A similar explanation presumably underlies the changes in cortical evoked potentials which have been described by Purpura, Girado, Smith, Callan, and Grundfest (1959), and many others, and the actions of GABA in this respect are probably universal throughout the nervous system.

Mention should briefly be made of extracts of brain which have been prepared by other groups of workers and which, in spite of certain differences in detail, appear likely to owe their actions to the presence of the same active materials as are contained in Factor I (McLennan, 1961b). The results have been reported by Pfeifer and Pataky (1955); Pataky and Pfeifer (1955); Lissák and Endröczi (1956); and Lissák, Endröczi, and Fábián (1957). Lissák, Endröczi, and Vincze (1961) have concluded that all the actions of their extracts cannot be explained in terms of GABA, again pointing out the probable relationship of these to Factor I.

Studies of inhibitory processes in invertebrates have also not yet yielded definite information on the chemical nature of the transmitters involved, with the exception of the role of acetylcholine in *Aplysia* ganglia mentioned above (p. 82). The finding that GABA has a potent effect upon the stretch receptor neurones of crayfish has, however, stimulated research in these directions in crustacea. GABA apparently can imitate perfectly the action of stimulation of the inhibitory nerve supply to the stretch receptor neurones (Kuffler and Edwards, 1958), causing an hyperpolarization of the cell and reduction in an evoked IPSP. The effect, like that of nerve stimulation, is largely blocked by picrotoxin. It is therefore very remarkable that Florey and Chapman (1961) have failed to detect GABA or glutamic decarboxylase, the enzyme responsible for its synthesis, in extracts of crustacean peripheral nerve. It has further been shown that extracts prepared from these nerves possess such a powerful inhibitory action that 15 per cent of their dry weight would have to be pure GABA in order to account for it (Florey and Biederman, 1960). Other authors have, however, reported the presence of GABA in crab nerve (Kravitz, Potter, and van Gelder, 1962a,b), and a discrepancy here which is unexplained at present

requires further investigation. The possibility, mentioned by these authors (1962b), does exist that GABA is formed during the extraction procedure from some unidentified material.

Florey (1960a) has chosen to call the crustacean material Substance I, as mentioned earlier, in order to differentiate it from the mammalian Factor I. Although the active ingredient of these extracts also is unidentified chemically, it appears to consist of a single substance and to possess a ninhydrin-positive group. Its behavior on paper chromatograms is not unlike that of one Factor I fraction of McLennan (1960a), but there is no other reason to think that the two are chemically identical.

Substance I (and GABA) are able also to bring about the inhibition of other structures in crayfish, and there is reasonable evidence to support the belief that the nerve extracts contain a transmitter of the inhibitory synapses of these animals. Florey (1961) lists this evidence as follows:

(1) Substance I imitates the action of inhibitory neurones in stretch receptors, cardiac ganglia, and at skeletal neuromuscular junctions.

(2) Its action is prevented by picrotoxin.

(3) It occurs exclusively in inhibitory neurones.

(4) It is released into a perfusion fluid only during stimulation of inhibitory nerves. This collection of data is far more complete than is the case for most other materials with which we have dealt in this chapter, and it remains only to identify the active ingredient of the nerve extracts.

It is worth emphasizing the fact that GABA is able to imitate apparently perfectly the action of the physiological transmitter substance, although it itself does not occur in the nerves whose action it mimics. It is therefore not enough to find a material which can duplicate the effects of nerve stimulation; the simple fact of its presence must be demonstrated before it can be claimed as a possible transmitter of synaptic action.

There is a considerable amount of published material which deals with the actions of GABA upon a wide variety of invertebrate nervous structures and even a few which would indicate that GABA and its beta-hydroxy derivative may not invariably have qualitatively similar actions (see, e.g., Vereshchagin, Sytinskii, and Tyshchenko, 1961). Nevertheless, this work cannot at present be related to synaptic events with any degree of assurance, and will therefore not be discussed here.

GABA AND GLUTAMIC ACID

Although, as we have seen, GABA cannot be equated with the inhibitory transmitter of mammalian brain and exerts its action upon neurones by causing a generalized change in their membrane permeability, yet this is a very marked effect which is, in all probability, of physiological significance. The very large concentrations of GABA which exist in the brain (see Table V) indicate that its presence in the environs of the cell could appreciably modify its excitability; and certain preliminary experiments, as, for example, those of Romanowski (1962), suggest that it may also have an action upon the elaboration of other humoral agents, such as acetylcholine. The concept of the importance of an environmental factor influencing neuronal activity has been made much more comprehensive by the findings of Curtis, Phillis, and Watkins (1960) and Curtis and Watkins (1960). They have shown that, whereas GABA and beta-alanine are depressant, the corresponding dicarboxylic acids, glutamic and aspartic, have a strong excitatory action. These authors have evidence that, as in the case of the depressant series, the enhanced excitability is due to a nonspecific effect upon the cell membrane leading to an increased conductance, but is unrelated to synaptic events. This reaction is not limited to these two pairs of compounds, for taurine-cysteic acid and homotaurine-homocysteic acid (Curtis, Phillis, and Watkins, 1961b) are also powerfully active and others are active to a lesser extent. The picture is, therefore, that these pairs of acids, of which the depressant member is the decarboxylated counterpart of the excitatory compound, may function as humoral regulators of the general level of excitability of central neurones, and the balance in their levels could exert a widespread measure of control. How this mechanism would be influenced is not clear and changes would presumably be comparatively slow; nevertheless, the possible importance of the system should certainly not be underestimated.

CEREBELLAR EXCITATORY FACTOR

Consideration of Table V will indicate that only very small amounts of most of the substances which we have considered in this chapter occur in the cerebellum. Nevertheless, this organ has a high neuronal density, and there is no reason to believe that its cells and the synapses upon them are different in their modes of action than are those elsewhere in the central nervous system. It follows therefore that the transmitter substances involved at cerebellar synapses are unidentified.

The only investigations which have been carried out with a view to understanding the nature of this material have been those of Crossland and his associates (Crossland and Mitchell, 1956; Crossland, Garven, and Mitchell, 1959; Crossland, 1960). They have prepared extracts of cerebellum free of acetylcholine, and have observed a pronounced enhancement of the electrical activity of the organ following the intra-arterial administration of this material. This property was found also in extracts of some other regions of the central nervous system which are low in choline acetylase activity, and which are therefore presumably comparatively free of cholinergic structures; and Crossland has suggested tentatively that this "cerebellar excitatory factor" may be the transmitter of non-cholinergic excitatory synapses throughout the brain. Its chemical nature is unknown, but it has been found to be stable in alkaline but unstable in hot acid solution, insoluble in acetone, dialyzable, and not affected by trypsin or chymotrypsin. It is obvious that any claim to a role as synaptic transmitter for the factor is premature; nevertheless, its occurrence in the cerebellum, where no other recognized transmitters exist, is reason enough for continued investigations into its nature and properties.

CONCLUSION

Various chemical entities and certain extracts of nervous tissue have been here considered as possible synaptic transmitter agents. With the exception of a number of cholinergic and rather fewer adrenergic systems, both vertebrate and invertebrate, the data supporting a certain type of chemical mediation in any given situation are quite inadequate, and in spite of the inherent difficulties the numerous problems to be solved are of great interest.

There is only one point which is striking and worthy of comment here. It has already been noted that the cerebellum is notably deficient in the commonly considered "neurohumoral agents," but it is equally true that some other areas, particularly the caudate nucleus and the hypothalamus, contain strikingly high amounts of most of these substances (see Table V). It is not clear what the functional significance of this may be; but it is difficult to escape the thought that these areas are acting as factories for the manufacture of these compounds which may not exert their final actions in their places of synthesis. If this should happen to be the case, then any attempt to draw conclusions from the distributions of the various materials and to relate these to known physiological or pharmacological facts could be very misleading. If, on the other hand, the compounds are acting as transmitters in the regions where they are found in high concentration, then it must not be forgotten that other areas of the brain in addition to the cerebellum are comparatively deficient in them—the cerebral cortex is a notable example —and the existence of yet unknown transmitters must probably be postulated. This aspect too must not be forgotten when attempts are made to interpret pharmacological data.

Chapter 7

CONCLUSION: PLASTICITY IN SYNAPTIC INTERACTIONS

Sufficient information has been discussed in detail in preceding chapters to indicate, in regard to the vertebrate central nervous system, to what an elaborate extent a fine control of the excitability of any given postsynaptic neurone is exerted. Some of the factors giving this control may be listed here as follows:

(1) The number and functional nature of synaptic contacts active at any moment;

(2) Temporal relationships between synaptic events;

(3) The location of synapses upon different portions of the postsynaptic neurone;

(4) The geometry of the synaptic regions, which will affect the time course of action of the synaptic transmitter;

(5) The chemical nature of the transmitters;

(6) The repetition rate of activation of any synapse, which changes the rate of production of transmitter;

(7) The degree of subliminal stimulation received from neighboring cells which are active;

(8) The balance between excitatory and depressant materials in the environment of the cell which may be influenced in turn by the over-all metabolism of the tissue.

Other factors could be added to this list, and the difficulty of predicting the subtle reactions of any cell in a physiological environment, other than when it is being "driven" by an artificially applied stimulus, is obvious enough.

However, this view of a neurone and its connections is by implication anatomically fixed, with flexibility conferred only by the reaction of the cell. It is difficult to conceive, in terms of this picture, how the nervous sys-

tem can perform such adaptive functions as are involved, for example, in the processes of learning. There are a few experimental findings relevant to these problems which will serve as a conclusion to this work.

The underlying theme of the preceding discussion in this book has been that, by and large, the fundamental processes governing synaptic events are qualitatively similar although they may differ very markedly in quantitative detail. However, there is one area in which this approach is probably unjustified, and this aspect has been barely touched upon in preceding chapters. Figure 7.1 gives a representation of the dendritic trees of some mammalian neurones. It is obvious that even in the simplest case, the surface area of the dendrites must be several times that of the soma. In our earlier considerations, only scant attention has been paid to this fact beyond noticing that, in motoneurones, those synaptic junctions situated far out upon the dendrites are likely to have a far smaller influence, at least in the generation of impulses, upon the reactivity of the neurone than those more proximally located.

It would seem only reasonable, having regard to Figure 7.1, that this cannot be generally true, and there is experimental justification for this statement. It has been widely believed that, normally, the dendrites of motoneurones are unable to conduct action potentials and that the spread of excitation through the dendritic system is by electrotonic propagation only. However, under the condition whereby chromatolysis of motoneurones is induced by section of the motor roots, it can be shown that synaptic excitation evokes partial spike

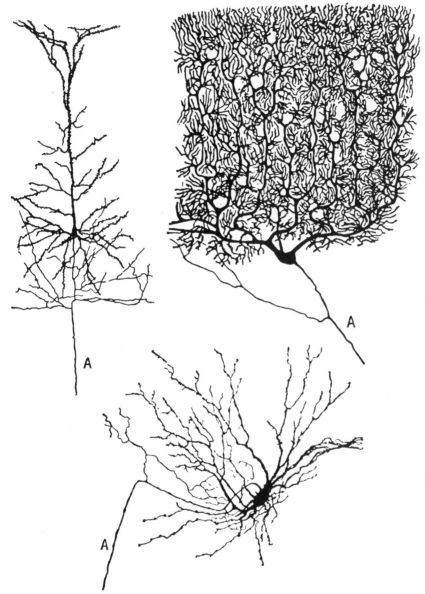

Figure 7.1. Drawings of typical neurones of the mammalian central nervous system to illustrate the diverse patterns of dendritic structure. Upper left, a pyramidal cell of the cerebral cortex; right, a Purkinje cell of the cerebellum; below, a motoneurone of the spinal cord. A in each case is the axon, which is cut off. (From Rall, 1962, by permission of the Rockefeller Institute.)

responses of both soma and dendrites (Eccles, Libet, and Young, 1958), and the implication is that under normal circumstances the dendritic membrane is likewise capable of such reaction. Indeed, the rate of propagation of dendritic action potentials has been measured at 0.7-1.0 m./sec. (Fatt, 1957).

In the pyramidal cells of the hippocampus and of other cortical areas, the question becomes still more important. In these cells the apical dendrites extend for a considerable distance and unlike those of motoneurones, the distal portions are thickly covered with synaptic endings. In order for these to affect the excitability of the axon hillock region of the soma, it would seem that some considerable degree of propagation of response is obligatory, and this has in fact been detected by Cragg and Hamlyn (1955). Clearly, such a mechanism must be even more important in the dendritic trees of the Purkinje cells. The extent of dendritic complexity and the arrangement of synapses upon the dendrites must therefore be recognized as another parameter yielding flexibility to the operations of the nervous system. Unfortunately, the electrical reactions of the dendrites are still far from understood, although the discussions given by Rall (1962) and others indicate great advances in this direction, and, as Eccles (1960) has remarked, "Up to twenty years ago it was customary to ascribe complex responses of the nervous system to the properties of the neuropil," whereas "It seems to me the neuropil has been superseded by dendrites, which now have the role of providing a superficial explanation of a wide variety of electrical phenomena."

One further point deserves mention in this connection. The concept of impulse propagation in dendrites leads to the possibility that the influence of one neurone upon another might be exerted at this level also, and van der Loos (1960) has shown that dendrodendritic junctions, where the elements approach each other at least as closely as is the case for conventional synapses, occur widely in the cerebral cortex. They exist between neurones of similar and of dissimilar types, and it is tempting to speculate that they represent another mode of interneuronal communication. The possibility also exists that the preferential enlargement of certain dendritic trees upon a neurone will contribute to the overall plasticity of the nervous system (Rall, 1962). Such dendritic growth has been observed following lesions of the cerebral cortex (Rose, Malis, Kruger, and Baker, 1960), and may be considered to occur during normal development as well.

There are several pieces of work germane to this book which bear upon the question of plasticity and development of function within the nervous system. It is clear that during the learning process a new nervous pathway must become established, one which possibly had no anatomical existence previously, or if it did exist was non-functioning. Since it is known that the ease of passage of an impulse through a synapse is facilitated by repetitive activity in the pathway, the latter alternative might involve only the provision of sufficient input in the dormant pathway to bring it into functional operation. However, it seems improbable that this can be the whole answer. The alternative has been expressed as follows (Hebb, 1949): "When an axon of cell 'A' is near enough to excite a cell 'B' and repeatedly or persistently takes part in firing it, some growth process or metabolic change takes place in one or both cells, such that 'A's

efficiency as one of the cells firing 'B' is increased." The hypothesis thus is that connections are formed during learning which did not exist before and that these then are of more or less permanent character. These propositions, while not completely proved, receive some support from neurophysiological investigations.

If synaptic efficiency is improved by use, it follows that there should be a decreased efficiency following a period in which the structures are completely inactive. This can be achieved for the monosynaptic spinal cord reflexes by section of the posterior roots distal to the posterior root ganglia. The operation has been found to lead to depression of the monosynaptic reflexes (Eccles and McIntyre, 1953), and the depressed reflexes respond by a more profound potentiation following high frequency stimulation (which persists for several hours) than do the reflexes in the control limb. Intracellular recording indicated that the EPSP's following the operative interference were reduced in size and that a prolonged increase in their amplitude was responsible for the post-tetanic potentiation (see Figure 7.2) (Eccles, Krnjević, and Miledi, 1959). Although part of these changes may be attributable to the shrinkage of the boutons which is observed after such an operation, the result following high frequency conditioning would seem unquestionably to indicate that the efficiency of the synapses is impaired by a period of disuse.

The converse to this experiment, namely one in which synapses are subjected to increased activation over a prolonged period and one which should therefore lead to their increased efficiency, is less easy to design. It has, however, been accomplished by Eccles and Westerman (1959), who severed some of the nerves leading to a synergic muscle group and capped them to prevent regeneration, in which case the remaining muscles of the group had to substitute for the whole in supporting the weight of the animal. An abnormal stress, leading to enhanced utilization of the remaining synaptic connections, is the result. In all animals so operated, the monosynaptic reflexes in the remaining muscles of the group were significantly increased over those of the opposite side, while the reflexes in muscles of other groups in the operated limb remained unchanged. It seems very probable therefore that an enhanced efficiency of synaptic action was, in fact, brought about by this procedure.

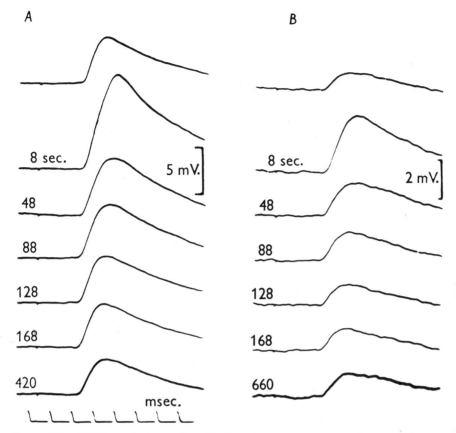

Figure 7.2.   EPSP's evoked in a flexor hallucis longus motoneurone by maximal group Ia afferent volleys in (*A*) flexor hallucis longus nerve and (*B*) flexor digitorum longus nerve, which had been severed 15 days previously. Top records were taken before, and succeeding ones at the indicated intervals after, a 10 sec. conditioning tetanus at 400/sec. Note the small EPSP resulting from the stimulation in *B* and its relatively very large post-tetanic potentiation. (From Eccles, Krnjević, and Miledi, 1959, by permission of the Journal of Physiology.)

There would thus seem to be direct experimental confirmation at the level of the spinal cord for one hypothesis invoked to explain learning processes in higher levels of the central nervous system. It is to be presumed that a particular sensory input results in the activation of a given pattern of central neurones, and that each time the same stimulus is presented, its passage through the pattern would be progressively easier as the efficiency of the synapses involved was increased by use. This is probably only a partial explanation of a complex process, but it does provide a reasonable basis on the neurophysiological level for this type of mental reaction.

Another aspect of neuronal function whose significance for higher functions is difficult to assess at present is what may be termed a differentiating effect of innervation. We have referred briefly to the effects of denervation

upon the subsequent reactions of synapses, which in time progress to atrophy of the denervated structure. What is implied here is an action of neurones in promoting the functional differentiation as well as development of the innervated tissue.

The skeletal muscles of cats may be divided into two groups: phasic, which respond by a quick twitch maximal in 25 to 30 msec., and tonic, which have a contraction time of about 80 msec. This division was first described by Ranvier (1874). In very young animals, however, the differentiation is not yet apparent. It has further been shown that the after-hyperpolarizations of the tonic motoneurones are considerably longer than of those of the cells which supply phasic muscles (Eccles, Eccles, and Lundberg, 1958), and thus the different reactions of the muscles can be correlated with the rate of firing of the motoneurones innervating them, since the length of the period of after-hyperpolarization limits the repetition rate of firing. It was felt to be of interest and importance "to reinvestigate the process of differentiation into fast and slow muscles, in an attempt to determine whether this appropriate matching of motoneurones to muscles was brought about by motoneurones influencing muscle differentiation, or *vice versa,* by muscle influencing motoneurones" (Buller, Eccles, and Eccles, 1960a).

Experiments were performed in which the muscle nerves of young animals were severed and reunited to muscles different from those from which they were taken, in such a way that a tonic nerve was applied to a muscle which in the adult would have become phasic, and *vice versa.* The results indicated that innervation of a muscle by phasic motoneurones would transform it into a fast-contracting one, while tonic motoneurones convert fast muscles to slow (Buller, Eccles, and Eccles, 1960b). There was no detectable effect of the "cross union" upon the motoneurones, and it was therefore concluded that some influence was exerted by the neurones which brought about the functional development of the innervated tissue. It was felt that this influence was most probably a substance formed in the cell and transported to the tissue by a flow down the axon.

This concept clearly might be of fundamental importance in the development of patterns within the central nervous system, for *a priori* there is no reason why one neurone could not affect the functional development of its successor in a chain as well as that of an effector organ. The influence would be permanent only so long as the innervation pattern remained intact or was not superseded by another, for Buller, Eccles, and Eccles (1960b) were able to show that the responses of the muscles could be altered by reinnervation even in adult cats.

This, therefore, raises one final matter relative to the plasticity of the nervous system, namely the extent to which synaptic junctions are fixed and invariable except insofar as their efficiency of action is concerned, i.e., whether the fine anatomical structure of the brain alters once growth is complete. There is an understandable tendency to regard a photomicrograph of a portion of the brain as representative of an architectural fixture, whereas it may be no more than a picture of the structures as they were at the moment of death. There is no evidence which can serve to supply definitive information on this point, but it must not be forgotten as a possibility. The sprouting of nerve endings is a familiar feature of regeneration in the nervous system, and this property would seem most probably to be involved in the physiological condition as well.

These brief considerations will serve as conclusion to this survey of synaptic transmission. Enough has been said to show how far our knowledge has advanced and how far it has yet to go before we approach a fuller understanding of that organ which Sir Charles Sherrington described as "an enchanted loom where millions of flashing shuttles weave a dissolving pattern, always a meaningful pattern though never an abiding one."

REFERENCES

Adrian, E. D. (1912). On the conductance of subnormal disturbances in normal nerve. J. Physiol., *45*, 389-412.

Adrian, R. H. (1960). Potassium chloride movement and the membrane potential of frog muscle. J. Physiol., *151*, 154-185.

Ahlquist, R. P. (1948). A study of the adrenotropic receptors. Am. J. Physiol., *153*, 586-600.

Alexandrowicz, J. S. (1951). Muscle receptor organs in the abdomen of *Homarus vulgaris* and *Palinurus vulgaris*. Quart. J. Micr. Sc., *92*, 163-200.

—— (1952). Receptor elements in the thoracic muscles of *Homarus vulgaris* and *Palinurus vulgaris*. Quart. J. Micr. Sc., *93*, 315-346.

Alexandrowicz, J. S., and Carlisle, D. B. (1953). Some experiments on the function of the pericardial organs in crustacea. J. Marine Biol. A., U. K., *32*, 175-192.

Amin, A. H., Crawford, T. B. B., and Gaddum, J. H. (1954). The distribution of substance P and 5-hydroxytryptamine in the central nervous system of the dog. J. Physiol., *126*, 596-618.

Andrews, T. M., and Holton, P. (1958). The substance P and adenosinetriphosphate (ATP) contents of sensory nerve on degeneration. J. Physiol., *143*, 45-46P.

Ansell, G. B., and Richter, D. (1954). A note on the free amino acid content of rat brain. Biochem. J., *57*, 70-73.

Araki, T., Eccles, J. C., and Ito, M. (1960). Correlation of the inhibitory postsynaptic potential of motoneurones with the latency and time course of inhibition of monosynaptic reflexes. J. Physiol., *154*, 354-377.

Araki, T., Ito, M., and Oscarsson, O. (1961). Anion permeability of the synaptic and non-synaptic motoneurone membrane. J. Physiol., *159*, 410-435.

Araki, T., and Otani, T. (1955). Responses of single motoneurones to direct stimulation in toad's spinal cord. J. Neurophysiol., *18*, 472-485.

Armin, J., and Grant, R. T. (1953). The artery of the denervated rabbit's ear as a sensitive pharmacological test object. J. Physiol., *121*, 593-602.

Arvanitaki, A., and Cardot, H. (1941). Observations sur la constitution des ganglions et conducteurs nerveux et sur l'isolement du soma neuronique vivant chez les mollusques Gastéropodes. Bull. histol. appliq. physiol., *18*, 133-144.

Arvanitaki, A., and Chalazonitis, N. (1960). Photopotentiels d'excitation et d'inhibition de différents somata identifiables (*Aplysia*). Bull. Inst. océanogr., *1164*, 1-83.

Asano, M., Noro, T., and Kuriaki, K. (1960). Inhibitory actions of γ-aminobutyrylcholine. Nature, *185*, 848-849.

Ashby, W., Garzoli, R. F., and Schuster, E. M. (1952). Relative distribution patterns of three brain enzymes, carbonic anhydrase, choline esterase and acetyl phosphatase. Am. J. Physiol., *170*, 116-120.

Axelsson, J., and Thesleff, S. (1959). A study of supersensitivity in denervated mammalian skeletal muscle. J. Physiol., *147*, 178-193.

Bacq, Z. M. (1935). Recherches sur la physiologie et la pharmacologie du système nerveux autonome. XIX. La choline-estérase chez les invertébrés. L'insensibilité des crustacés à l'acétylcholine. Arch. internat. physiol., *42*, 47-60.

—— (1939). Action de l'ésérine chez les holothuries et chez les ascidies. Présence de nerfs cholinergiques chez les holothuries. Arch. internat. physiol., *49*, 25-32.

Bacq, Z. M., and Brown, G. L. (1937). Pharmacological experiments on mammalian voluntary muscle, in relation to the theory of chemical transmission. J. Physiol., *89*, 45-60.

Bacq, Z. M., and Coppée, G. (1937a). Réaction des vers et des mollusques à l'ésérine. Existence de nerfs cholinergiques chez les vers. Arch. internat. physiol., *45*, 310-324.

——, —— (1937b). Contraste entre les vers et les mollusques en ce qui concerve leur réaction à l'ésérine. C. R. Soc. Biol., Paris, *125*, 1059-1060.

Barger, G., and Dale, H. H. (1910). Chemical structure and sympathomimetic action of amines. J. Physiol., *41*, 19-59.

Barnett, R. J. (1962). The fine structural localization of acetylcholinesterase at the myoneural junction. J. Cell Biol., *12*, 247-262.

Barsoum, G. S. (1935). The acetylcholine equivalent of nervous tissues. J. Physiol., *84*, 259-262.

Bass, A. (1914). Über eine Wirkung des Adrenalins auf das Gehirn. Ztschr. ges. Neurol. Psychiat., *26*, 600-601.

Baxter, C. F., and Roberts, E. (1959). Elevation of γ-aminobutyric acid in rat brain with hydroxylamine. Proc. Soc. Exper. Biol., N.Y., *101*, 811-815.

——, —— (1960). Demonstration of thiosemicarbazide-induced convulsions in rats with elevated brain levels of γ-aminobutyric acid. Proc. Soc. Exper. Biol., N.Y., *104*, 426-427.

——, —— (1961). Elevation of γ-aminobutyric acid in brain: selective inhibition of γ-aminobutyric acid-α-ketoglutaric acid transaminase. J. Biol. Chem., *236*, 3287-3294.

Bayliss, W. M. (1901). On the origin from the spinal cord of the vasodilator fibres of the hind limb, and on the nature of these fibres. J. Physiol., *26*, 173-209.

Bazemore, A. W., Elliott, K. A. C., and Florey, E. (1957). Isolation of Factor I. J. Neurochem., *1*, 334-339.

Beleslin, D., Radmanović, B., and Varagić, V. (1960). The effect of substance P on the superior cervical ganglion of the cat. Brit. J. Pharmacol., *15*, 10-13.

Belleau, B. (1960). Relationships between agonists, antagonists and receptor sites, in: *Adrenergic Mechanisms* (J. R. Vane, ed.). London, Churchill, pp. 223-245.

Bennett, M. V. L., Crain, S. M., and Grundfest, H. (1959). Electrophysiology of supramedullary neurons in *Spheroides maculatus*. II. Properties of the electrically excitable membrane. J. Gen. Physiol., *43*, 189-219.

Berl, S., and Waelsch, H. (1958). Determination of glutamic acid, glutamine, glutathione and γ-aminobutyric acid and their distribution in brain tissue. J. Neurochem., *3*, 161-169.

Bernhard, C. G., Gray, J. A. B., and Widén, L. (1953). The difference in response of monosynaptic extensor and monosynaptic flexor reflexes to d-tubocurarine and adrenaline. Acta physiol. scandinav., *29*, Suppl. 106, 73-78.

Bernhard, C. G., and Skoglund, C. R. (1953). Potential changes in spinal cord following intra-arterial administration of adrenaline and noradrenaline as compared with acetylcholine effects. Acta physiol. scandinav., *29*, Suppl. 106, 435-454.

Bernhard, C. G., Skoglund, C. R., and Therman, P. O. (1947). Studies of the potential level in the ventral root under varying conditions. Acta physiol. scandinav., *14*, Suppl. 47, #8.

Bernhard, W., and Rouiller, C. (1956). Close topographical relationship between mitochondria and ergastoplasm of liver cells in a definite phase of cellular activity. J. Biophys. Biochem. Cytol., *2*, Suppl., 73-78.

Bernstein, J. (1868). Über den zeitliche Verlauf der negativen Schwankung des Nervenstroms. Arch. ges. Physiol., *1*, 173-207.

Bertler, Å. (1961). Occurrence and localization of catechol amines in human brain. Acta physiol. scandinav., *51*, 97-101.

Bertler, Å., and Rosengren, E. (1959). Occurrence and distribution of catechol amines in brain. Acta physiol. scandinav., *47*, 350-361.

Bindman, L. J., Lippold, O. C. J., and Redfearn, J. W. T. (1962). The non-selective blocking action of γ-aminobutyric acid on the sensory cerebral cortex of the rat. J. Physiol., *162*, 105-120.

Birkhäuser, H. (1940). Fermente in Gehirn geistig normaler Menschen. Helvet. chim. acta, *23*, 1071-1086.

Birks, R. I. (1961). Sub-cellular structures within motor-nerve terminals at frog myoneural junctions. Abstr. internat. biophys. Congr., Stockholm, p. 249.

—— (1962). The effects of a cardiac glycoside on subcellular structures within nerve cells and their processes in sympathetic ganglia and skeletal muscle. Canad. J. Biochem. Physiol., *40*, 303-315.

Birks, R. I., and Brown, L. M. (1960). A method for locating the cholinesterase of a mammalian myoneural junction by electron microscopy. J. Physiol., *152*, 5-7P.

Birks, R., Huxley, H. E., and Katz, B. (1960). The fine structure of the neuromuscular junction of the frog. J. Physiol., *150*, 134-144.

Bishop, P. O., Burke, W., and Hayhow, W. R. (1959). Lysergic acid diethylamide block of lateral geniculate synapses and relief by repetitive stimulation. Exper. Neurol., *1*, 556-568.

Blackman, J. G., Ginsborg, B. L., and Ray, C. (1962). The release of acetylcholine at a ganglionic synapse. J. Physiol., *162*, 58-59P.

Blair, M. R., and Clark, B. B. (1956). An evaluation of the action of substance P on the jejunum of the rabbit. J. Pharmacol., *117*, 467-477.

Blaschko, H., Born, G. V. R., D'Iorio, A., and Eade, N. R. (1956). Observations on the distribution of catechol amines and adenosine triphosphate in the bovine adrenal medulla. J. Physiol., *133*, 548-557.

Bodian, D. (1937). The structure of the vertebrate synapse. A study of the axon endings on Mauthner's cell and neighboring centers in the goldfish. J. Comp. Neurol., *68*, 117-159.

—— (1952). Introductory survey of neurons. Cold Spr. Harb. Symp. Quant. Biol., *17*, 1-13.

Bogdanski, D. F., Weissbach, H., and Udenfriend, S. (1956). The distribution of serotonin, 5-hydroxytryptophan decarboxylase, and monoamine oxidase in brain. J. Neurochem., *1*, 272-278.

——, ——, —— (1958). Pharmacological studies with the serotonin precursor, 5-hydroxytryptophan. J. Pharmacol., *122*, 182-194.

Boistel, J., and Fatt, P. (1958). Membrane permeability change during inhibitory transmitter action in crustacean muscle. J. Physiol., *144*, 176-191.

Bonta, I. L., Wijmenga, H. G., and Hohensee, F. (1961). Über die Wirkung von Substanz P und anderen Hirnextrakten auf des Zentralnervensystem. Acta physiol. et pharmacol. neerl., *10*, 114-118.

Bonvallet, M., and Minz, B. (1938) Action des médiateurs chimiques sur la réflexe linguo-maxillaire. Action de l'adrénaline. C. R. Soc. Biol., Paris, *128*, 162-164.

Boycott, B. B., Gray, E. G., and Guillery, R. W. (1961). Synaptic structure and its alteration with environmental temperature: a study by light and electron microscopy of the central nervous system of lizards. Proc. Roy. Soc., London *B:154*, 151-172.

Boyd, I. A., and Martin, A. R. (1956a). Spontaneous subthreshold activity at mammalian neuromuscular junctions. J. Physiol., *132*, 61-73.

——, —— (1956b). The end-plate potential in mammalian muscle. J. Physiol., *132*, 74-91.

Bradley, K., Easton, D. M., and Eccles, J. C. (1953). An investigation of primary or direct inhibition. J. Physiol., 122, 474-488.

Bradley, K., and Eccles, J. C. (1953). Analysis of the fast afferent impulses from thigh muscles. J. Physiol., 122, 462-473.

Brock, L. G., Coombs, J. S., and Eccles, J. C. (1952). The recording of potentials from motoneurones with an intracellular electrode. J. Physiol., 117, 431-460.

Brodie, B. B., and Shore, P. A. (1957). A concept for a role of serotonin and norepinephrine as chemical mediators in the brain. Ann. N.Y. Acad. Sc., 66, 631-642.

Broghammer, H., Takagi, K., and Schaefer, H. (1957). Die Wirkung von Lysergsäure-Diäthylamid (LSD) und Urethan auf die Tätigkeit eines sympathischen Ganglions. Arch. Exper. Path. Pharmakol., 230, 358-366.

Brooks, C. McC., and Koizumi, K. (1956). Origin of the dorsal root reflex. J. Neurophysiol., 19, 61-74.

Brooks, V. B. (1956). An intracellular study of the action of repetitive nerve volleys and of botulinum toxin on miniature end-plate potentials. J. Physiol., 134, 264-277.

Brown, G. L. (1937). The actions of acetylcholine on denervated mammalian and frog's muscles. J. Physiol., 89, 438-461.

Brown, G. L., Bülbring, E., and Burns, B. D. (1948). The action of adrenaline on mammalian skeletal muscle. J. Physiol., 107, 115-128.

Brown, G. L., Dale, H. H., and Feldberg, W. (1936). Reactions of the normal mammalian muscle to acetylcholine and to eserine. J. Physiol., 87, 394-424.

Brown, G. L., Davies, B. N., and Ferry, C. B. (1961). The effect of neuronal rest on the output of sympathetic transmitter from the spleen. J. Physiol., 159, 365-380.

Brown, G. L., Davies, B. N., and Gillespie, J. S. (1958). The release of chemical transmitter from the sympathetic nerves of the intestine of the cat. J. Physiol., 143, 41-54.

Brown, G. L., Goffart, M., and Vianna Dias, M. (1950). The effects of adrenaline and of sympathetic stimulation on the demarcation potential of mammalian skeletal muscle. J. Physiol., 111, 184-194.

Brown, G. L., and Gray, J. A. B. (1948). Some effects of nicotine-like substances and their relation to sensory nerve endings. J. Physiol., 107, 306-317.

Bülbring, E. (1944). Action of adrenaline on transmission in the superior cervical ganglion. J. Physiol., 103, 55-67.

—— (1946). Observations on the isolated phrenic nerve diaphragm preparation of the rat. Brit. J. Pharmacol., 1, 38-61.

Bülbring, E., and Burn, J. H. (1941). Observations bearing on synaptic transmission by acetylcholine in the spinal cord. J. Physiol., 100, 337-368.

——, —— (1942). An action of adrenaline on transmission in sympathetic ganglia, which may play a part in shock. J. Physiol., 101, 289-303.

Buller, A. J., Eccles, J. C., and Eccles, R. M. (1960a). Differentiation of fast and slow muscles in the cat hind limb. J. Physiol., 150, 399-416.

——, ——, —— (1960b). Interactions between motoneurones and muscles in respect of the characteristic speeds of their responses. J. Physiol., 150, 417-439.

Bullock, T. H. (1952). The invertebrate neuron junction. Cold Spr. Harb. Symp. Quant. Biol., 17, 267-273.

—— (1961). On the anatomy of the giant neurons of the visceral ganglion of Aplysia, in: Nervous Inhibition (E. Florey, ed.), Oxford, Pergamon Press, pp. 233-240.

Bullock, T. H., and Hagiwara, S. (1957). Intracellular recording from the giant synapse of the squid. J. Gen. Physiol., 40, 565-577.

Burgen, A. S. V., and Chipman, L. M. (1951). Cholinesterase and succinic dehydrogenase in the central nervous system of the dog. J. Physiol., 114, 296-305.

Burgen, A. S. V., Dickens, F., and Zatman, L. J. (1949). The action of botulinum toxin on the neuromuscular junction. J. Physiol., 109, 10-24.

Burke, W., and Ginsborg, B. L. (1956). The electrical properties of the slow muscle fibre membrane. J. Physiol., 132, 586-598.

Burn, J. H., Leach, E. H., Rand, M. J., and Thompson, J. W. (1959). Peripheral effects of nicotine and acetylcholine resembling those of sympathetic stimulation. J. Physiol., 148, 332-352.

Burn, J. H., and Rand, M. J. (1958a). Action of nicotine on the heart. Brit. M. J., 1, 137-139.

——, —— (1958b). Noradrenaline in artery walls and its dispersal by reserpine. Brit. M. J., 1, 903-908.

——, —— (1960). Sympathetic postganglionic cholinergic fibres. Brit. J. Pharmacol., 15, 56-66.

Burnstock, G., and Holman, M. E. (1961). The transmission of excitation from autonomic nerve to smooth muscle. J. Physiol., 155, 115-133.

——, —— (1962a). Spontaneous potentials at sympathetic nerve endings in smooth muscle. J. Physiol., 160, 446-460.

——, —— (1962b). Effect of denervation and of reserpine treatment on transmission at sympathetic nerve endings. J. Physiol., 160, 461-469.

Buser, P., and Albe-Fessard, D. (1957). Explorations intracellulaire au niveau du cortex sensorimoteur du chat. Colloques Internat. C.N.R.S., Paris, 67, 333-352.

Caesar, R. (1959). Elektronenmikroskopische Beobachtungen zum Verhalten der marklösen Nervenfasern im glatten Muskelgewebe. Anat. Gesellsch., 55, 90-96.

Caesar, R., Edwards, G. A., and Ruska, H. (1957). Architecture and nerve supply of mammalian smooth muscle. J. Biophys. Biochem. Cytol., 3, 867-877.

Cajal, S. R. (1890). Sur l'origine et les ramifications des fibres nerveuses de la moelle embryonnaire. Anat. Anz., 5, 111-119.

—— (1934). Les preuves objectives de l'unité anatomique des cellules nerveuses. Trab. Lab. Invest. biol. Univ. Madrid, 29, 1-137.

—— (1955). Histologie du Système Nerveux de l'Homme et des Vertébrés. Tome II. Madrid, Consejo Superior de Investigaciones Cientificas.

Cannon, W. B., and Rosenblueth, A. (1933). Sympathin E and Sympathin I. Am. J. Physiol., 104, 557-574.

——, —— (1949). The Supersensitivity of Denervated Structures. New York, The Macmillan Co.

Cannon, W. B., and Uridil, J. E. (1921). Studies on the conditions of activity in endocrine glands. VIII. Some effects on the denervated heart of stimulating the nerves of the liver. Am. J. Physiol., 58, 353-354.

Carlisle, D. B. (1956). An indole-alkylamine regulating heart-beat in crustacea. Biochem. J., 63, 32-33P.

―――― (1962). (In course of publication.)

Carlsson, A. (1959). The occurrence, distribution and physiological role of catecholamines in the nervous system. Pharmacol. Rev., 11, 490-493.

Casselman, W. G. B. (1961). Some contributions of cell biology to the study of muscle diseases. Merck Lecture at the University of British Columbia, Oct. 19.

Cerletti, A., and Rothlin, E. (1955). Role of 5-hydroxytryptamine in mental diseases and its antagonism to lysergic acid derivatives. Nature, 176, 785-786.

Chaillet, F., Phillipot, E., and Schlag, J. (1961). Études des propriétés pharmacologiques des esters méthylique et éthylique du chlorure de γ-butyrobétaine. Arch. internat. pharmacodyn., 133, 333-337.

Chalazonitis, N. (1961). Chemopotentials in giant nerve cells (Aplysia fasciata), in: Nervous Inhibition (E. Florey, ed.). Oxford, Pergamon Press, pp. 179-193.

Chalazonitis, N., and Arvanitaki, A. (1961). Potentiels générateurs par activation méchanique de la membrane somatique. C. R. Acad. Sc., Paris, 252, 4046-4048.

Chalazonitis, N., and Sugaya, E. (1958). Stimulation-inhibition des neurones géants identifiables d'Aplysia par l'anhydride carbonique. C. R. Acad. Sc., Paris, 247, 1657-1659.

Chang, H.-T. (1953). Similarity in action between curare and strychnine on cortical neurons. J. Neurophysiol., 16, 221-233.

Chang, V., and Rand, M. J. (1960). Transmission failure in sympathetic nerves produced by hemicholinium. Brit. J. Pharmacol., 15, 588-600.

Cohen, L. H., Thale, T., and Tissenbaum, M. J. (1944). Acetylcholine treatment of schizophrenia. Arch. Neurol. & Psychiat., Chicago, 51, 171-175.

Conway, E. J. (1947). Exchanges of K, Na and H ions between the cell and its environment. Irish J. M. Sc., 6th series, pp. 654-680.

Coombs, J. S., Curtis, D. R., and Eccles, J. C. (1956). Time courses of motoneuronal responses. Nature, 178, 1049-1050.

―――, ―――, ――― (1957). The generation of impulses in motoneurones. J. Physiol., 139, 232-249.

―――, ―――, ――― (1959). The electrical constants of the motoneurone membrane. J. Physiol., 145, 505-528.

Coombs, J. S. Curtis, D. R., and Landgren, S. (1956). Spinal cord potentials generated by impulses in muscle and cutaneous afferent fibres. J. Neurophysiol., 19, 452-467.

Coombs, J. S., Eccles, J. C., and Fatt, P. (1955a). The electrical properties of the motoneurone membrane. J. Physiol., 130, 291-325.

―――, ―――, ――― (1955b). The specific ionic conductances and the ionic movements across the motoneuronal membrane that produce the inhibitory post-synaptic potential. J. Physiol., 130, 326-373.

―――, ―――, ――― (1955c). Excitatory synaptic action in motoneurones. J. Physiol., 130, 374-395.

―――, ―――, ――― (1955d). The inhibitory suppression of reflex discharges from motoneurones. J. Physiol., 130, 396-413.

Couteaux, R. (1958). Morphological and cytochemical observations on the post-synaptic membrane at motor end-plates and ganglionic synapses. Exper. Cell Res., Suppl., 5, 294-322.

Couteaux, R., and Nachmansohn, D. (1940). Changes of cholinesterase at end plates of voluntary muscle following section of sciatic nerve. Proc. Soc. Exper. Biol., N.Y., 43, 177-181.

Cragg, B. G., and Hamlyn, L. H. (1955). Action potentials of the pyramidal neurones in the hippocampus of the rabbit. J. Physiol., 129, 608-627.

Creutzfeldt, O., Baumgartner, G., and Schoen, L. (1956). Reaktionen einzelner Neurone des sensomotorischen Cortex nach elektrischen Reizen. I. Hemmung und Erregung nach direkten und kontralateralen Einzelreizen. Arch. Psychiat., 194, 597-619.

Crossland, J. (1960). Chemical transmission in the central nervous system. J. Pharm. & Pharmacol., 12, 1-36.

Crossland, J., Garven, J. D., and Mitchell, J. F. (1959). Characterization and distribution in the central nervous system of the cerebellar excitatory factor. J. Physiol., 148, 20-21P.

Crossland, J., and Mitchell, J. F. (1956). The effect on the electrical activity of the cerebellum of a substance present in cerebellar extracts. J. Physiol., 132, 391-405.

Crum-Brown, A., and Fraser, T. R. (1869). On the connection between chemical constitution and physiological action. I. On the physiological action of the salts of the ammonium basis derived from Strychnia, Brucia, Thebaia, Codeia, Morphia, and Nicotia. Tr. Roy. Soc. Edinburgh, 25, 151-203. II. On the physiological action of the ammonium basis derived from Atropia and Cornia. Ibid., 693-739.

Cummins, J. T., and McIlwain, H. (1961). Electrical pulses and the potassium and other ions of isolated cerebral tissues. Biochem. J., 79, 330-341.

Curtis, D. R. (1959). Pharmacological investigations upon inhibition of spinal motoneurones. J. Physiol., 145, 175-192.

―――― (1962). The action of 3-hydroxytyramine and some tryptamine derivatives upon spinal neurones. Nature, 194, 292.

Curtis, D. R., and Davis, R. (1961). A central action of 5-hydroxytryptamine and noradrenaline. Nature, 192, 1083-1084.

―――, ――― (1962). Pharmacological studies upon neurones of the lateral geniculate nucleus of the cat. Brit. J. Pharmacol., 18, 217-246.

Curtis, D. R., and Eccles, J. C. (1959). The time courses of excitatory and inhibitory synaptic actions. J. Physiol., 145, 529-546.

―――, ――― (1960). Synaptic action during and after repetitive stimulation. J. Physiol., 150, 374-398.

Curtis, D. R., Eccles, J. C., and Eccles, R. M. (1957). Pharmacological studies on spinal reflexes. J. Physiol., 136, 420-434.

Curtis, D. R., Eccles, J. C., and Lundberg, A. (1958). Intracellular recording from cells in Clarke's column. Acta physiol. scandinav., 43, 303-314.

Curtis, D. R., and Eccles, R. M. (1958a). The excitation of Renshaw cells by pharmacological agents applied electrophoretically. J. Physiol., 141, 435-445.

―――, ――― (1958b). The effect of diffusional barriers upon the pharmacology of cells within the central nervous system. J. Physiol., 141, 446-463.

Curtis, D. R., and Koizumi, K. (1961). Chemical transmitter substances in brain stem of cat. J. Neurophysiol., 24, 80-90.

Curtis, D. R., and Krnjević, K., and Miledi, R. (1958). Crossed inhibition of sacral motoneurones. J. Neurophysiol., *21*, 319-326.

Curtis, D. R., Phillis, J. W., and Watkins, J. C. (1959). The depression of spinal neurones by γ-amino-*n*-butyric acid and β-alanine. J. Physiol., *146*, 185-203.

————, ————, ———— (1960). The chemical excitation of spinal neurones by certain acidic amino acids. J. Physiol., *150*, 656-682.

————, ————, ———— (1961a). Cholinergic and non-cholinergic transmission in the mammalian spinal cord. J. Physiol., *158*, 296-323.

————, ————, ———— (1961b). Actions of amino-acids on the isolated hemisected spinal cord of the toad. Brit. J. Pharmacol., *16*, 262-283.

Curtis, D. R., and Watkins, J. C. (1960). The excitation and depression of spinal neurones by structurally related amino acids. J. Neurochem., *6*, 117-141.

Dale, H. H. (1914). The action of certain esters and ethers of choline, and their relation to muscarine. J. Pharmacol., *6*, 147-190.

———— (1934). Chemical transmission of the effects of nerve impulses. Brit. M. Bull., *1*, 835-841.

———— (1935). Pharmacology and nerve-endings. Proc. Roy. Soc. Med., *28*, 319-332.

Dale, H. H., and Dudley, H. W. (1929). The presence of histamine and acetylcholine in the spleen of the ox and the horse. J. Physiol., *68*, 97-123.

Dale, H. H., Feldberg, W., and Vogt, M. (1936). Release of acetylcholine at voluntary motor nerve endings. J. Physiol., *86*, 353-380.

Davson, H. (1955). A comparative study of the aqueous humour and cerebrospinal fluid in the rabbit. J. Physiol., *129*, 111-133.

———— (1957). *Physiology of the Ocular and Cerebrospinal Fluids.* London, Churchill.

de Castro, F. (1951). Aspects anatomiques de la transmission synaptique ganglionnaire chez les mammifères. Arch. internat. physiol., *59*, 479-513.

de Lorenzo, A. J. D. (1961). Electron microscopy of the cerebral cortex. I. The ultrastructure and histochemistry of synaptic junctions. Bull. Johns Hopkins Hosp., *108*, 258-279.

de Robertis, E. (1956). Submicroscopic changes of the synapse after nerve section in the acoustic ganglion of the guinea pig. J. Biophys. Biochem. Cytol., *2*, 503-512.

———— (1958). Submicroscopic morphology and function of the synapse. Exper. Cell Res., Suppl., *5*, 347-369.

———— (1959). Submicroscopic morphology of the synapse. Internat. Rev. Cytol., *8*, 61-96.

———— (1962). Some old and new concepts of brain structure. World Neurol., *3*, 98-111.

de Robertis, E., and Bennett, H. S., (1954). Submicroscopic vesicular component in the synapse. Fed. Proc., *13*, 35.

————, ———— (1955). Some features of the submicroscopic morphology of synapses in frog and earthworm. J. Biophys. Biochem. Cytol., *1*, 47-58.

de Robertis, E., and Franchi, C. M. (1956). Electron microscope observations on synaptic vesicles in synapses of the retinal rods and cones. J. Biophys. Biochem. Cytol., *2*, 307-318.

de Robertis, E., Pellegrino de Iraldi, A., Rodriguez de Lores Arnaiz, G., and Salganicoff, L. (1962). Cholinergic and non-cholinergic nerve endings in rat brain. I. Isolation and subcellular distribution of acetylcholine and acetylcholinesterase. J. Neurochem., *9*, 23-35.

del Castillo, J., and Engbaek, L. (1954). The nature of the neuromuscular block produced by magnesium. J. Physiol., *124*, 370-384.

del Castillo, J., and Katz, B. (1954). Quantal components of the end-plate potential. J. Physiol., *124*, 560-573.

————, ———— (1957). Modifications de la membrane produites par des influx nerveux dans la région du pace-maker du coeur. Colloques Internat. C.N.R.S., Paris, *67*, 271-279.

del Castillo, J., and Stark, L. (1952). The effect of calcium ions on the motor end-plate potentials. J. Physiol., *116*, 507-515.

Dell, P. (1960). Intervention of an adrenergic mechanism during brain stem reticular activation, in: *Adrenergic Mechanisms* (J. R. Vane, ed.). London, Churchill, pp. 393-409.

Dell, P., Bonvallet, M., and Hugelin, A. (1954). Tonus sympathique, adrénaline et contrôle réticulaire de la motricité spinale. Electroencephalog. & Clin. Neurophysiol., *6*, 599-618.

Dikshit, B. B. (1934). The production of cardiac irregularities by excitation of the hypothalamic centres. J. Physiol., *81*, 382-394.

Dixon, W. E. (1906). Vagus inhibition. Brit. M. J., *2*, 1807.

———— (1907). On the mode of action of drugs. Med. Magazine, *16*, 454-457.

Domer, F. R., and Feldberg, W. (1960). Some central actions of adrenaline and noradrenaline when administered into the cerebral ventricles, in: *Adrenergic Mechanisms* (J. R. Vane, ed.). London, Churchill, pp. 386-392.

Douglas, W. W., and Ritchie, J. M. (1960). The excitatory action of acetylcholine on cutaneous non-myelinated fibres. J. Physiol., *150*, 501-514.

Douglas, W. W., and Rubin, R. P. (1961a). The role of calcium in the secretory response of the adrenal medulla to acetylcholine. J. Physiol., *159*, 40-57.

————, ———— (1961b). Mechanism of nicotinic action at the adrenal medulla: calcium as a link in stimulus-secretion coupling. Nature, *192*, 1087-1089.

Draper, M. H., and Weidmann, S. (1951). Cardiac resting and action potentials recorded with an intracellular electrode. J. Physiol., *115*, 74-94.

Dráskoci, M., Feldberg, W., and Haranath, P. S. R. K. (1960). Passage of circulating adrenaline into perfused cerebral ventricles and subarachnoidal space. J. Physiol., *150*, 34-49.

duBois-Reymond, E. (1860). *Untersuchungen über thierische Elektricität.* Berlin, G. Reimer. 368 pp.

Dudel, J., and Kuffler, S. W. (1961a). The quantal nature of transmission and spontaneous miniature potentials at the crayfish neuromuscular junction. J. Physiol., *155*, 514-529.

————, ———— (1961b). Mechanism of facilitation at the crayfish neuromuscular junction. J. Physiol., *155*, 530-542.

————, ———— (1961c). Presynaptic inhibition at the crayfish neuromuscular junction. J. Physiol., *155*, 543-562.

Eccles, J. C. (1957). *The Physiology of Nerve Cells.* Baltimore, Johns Hopkins Press.

———— (1960). The properties of the dendrites, in: *Structure and Function of the Cerebral Cortex* (D. B. Tower and J. P. Schadé, eds.). Amsterdam, Elsevier, pp. 192-202.

——— (1961a). Membrane time constants of cat moto-neurons and time courses of synaptic action. Exper. Neurol., *4*, 1-22.

——— (1961b). The mechanism of synaptic transmission. Ergebn. Physiol., *51*, 299-430.

——— (1962). Spinal neurones: synaptic connexions in relation to chemical transmitters and pharmacological responses, in: *A Symposium on Pharmacological Analysis of Central Nervous Action* (W. D. M. Paton, ed.). Oxford, Pergamon Press.

Eccles, J. C., Eccles, R. M., and Fatt, P. (1956). Pharmacological investigations on a central synapse operated by acetylcholine. J. Physiol., *131*, 154-169.

Eccles, J. C., Eccles, R. M., Iggo, A., and Lundberg, A. (1961). Electrophysiological investigations on Renshaw cells. J. Physiol., *159*, 461-478.

Eccles, J. C., Eccles, R. M., and Lundberg, A. (1957). Synaptic actions on motoneurones caused by impulses in Golgi tendon organ afferents. J. Physiol., *138*, 227-252.

———, ——— (1958). The action potentials of the alpha motoneurones supplying fast and slow muscles. J. Physiol., *142*, 275-291.

———, ———, ——— (1960). Types of neurone in and around the intermediate nucleus of the lumbosacral cord. J. Physiol., *154*, 89-114.

Eccles, J. C., Eccles, R. M., and Magni, F. (1960). Presynaptic inhibition in the spinal cord. J. Physiol., *154*, 28P.

———, ———, ——— (1961). Central inhibitory action attributable to presynaptic depolarization produced by muscle afferent volleys. J. Physiol., *159*, 147-166.

Eccles, J. C., Fatt, P., and Koketsu, K. (1954). Cholinergic and inhibitory synapses in a pathway from motor-axon collaterals to motoneurones. J. Physiol., *126*, 524-562.

Eccles, J. C., Fatt, P., and Landgren, S. (1956). The central pathway for the direct inhibitory action of impulses in the large muscle afferent fibres. J. Neurophysiol., *19*, 75-98.

Eccles, J. C., Fatt, P., Landgren, S., and Winsbury, G. J. (1954). Spinal cord potentials generated by volleys in the large muscle afferents. J. Physiol., *125*, 590-606.

Eccles, J. C., Hubbard, J. I., and Oscarsson, O. (1961). Intracellular recording from cells of the ventral spinocerebellar tract. J. Physiol., *158*, 486-516.

Eccles, J. C., and Jaeger, J. C. (1958). The relationship between the mode of operation and the dimensions of the junctional regions at synapses and motor end-organs. Proc. Roy. Soc. London B:*148*, 38-56.

Eccles, J. C., Katz, B., and Kuffler, S. W. (1942). Effect of eserine on neuromuscular transmission. J. Neurophysiol., *5*, 211-230.

Eccles, J. C., Kostyuk, P. G., and Schmidt, R. F. (1962a). Central pathways responsible for depolarization of primary afferent fibres. J. Physiol., *161*, 237-257.

———, ———, ——— (1962b). Presynaptic inhibition of the central actions of flexor reflex afferents. J. Physiol., *161*, 258-281.

Eccles, J. C., and Kozak, W., and Magni, F. (1961) Dorsal root reflexes of muscle Group I afferent fibres. J. Physiol., *159*, 128-146.

Eccles, J. C., Krnjević, K., and Miledi, R. (1959). Delayed effects of peripheral severance of afferent nerve fibres on the efficacy of their central synapses. J. Physiol., *145*, 204-220.

Eccles, J. C., Libet, B., and Young, R. R. (1958). The behaviour of chromatolysed motoneurones studied by intracellular recording. J. Physiol., *143*, 11-40.

Eccles, J. C., and McIntyre, A. K. (1953). The effects of disuse and of activity on mammalian spinal reflexes. J. Physiol., *121*, 492-516.

Eccles, J. C., Magni, F., and Willis, W. D. (1962). Depolarization of central terminals of Group I afferent fibres from muscle. J. Physiol., *160*, 62-93.

Eccles, J. C., Oscarsson, O., and Willis, W. D. (1961). Synaptic action of Group I and II afferent fibres of muscle on the cells of the dorsal spinocerebellar tract. J. Physiol., *158*, 517-543.

Eccles, J. C., Schmidt, R. F., and Willis, W. D. (1962). Presynaptic inhibition of the spinal monosynaptic reflex pathway. J. Physiol., *161*, 282-297.

Eccles, R. M. (1955). Intracellular potentials recorded from a mammalian sympathetic ganglion. J. Physiol., *130*, 572-584.

Eccles, R. M., and Libet, B. (1961). Origin and blockade of the synaptic responses of curarized sympathetic ganglia. J. Physiol., *157*, 484-503.

Eccles, R. M., and Lundberg, A. (1959). Synaptic actions in motoneurones by afferents which may evoke the flexion reflex. Arch. ital. biol., *97*, 199-221.

Eccles, R. M., and Westerman, R. A. (1959). Enhanced synaptic function due to excess use. Nature, *184*, 460-461.

Edwards, C., and Kuffler, S. W. (1959). The blocking effect of γ-aminobutyric acid (GABA) and the action of related compounds on single nerve cells. J. Neurochem., *4*, 19-30.

Edwards, C., and Ottoson, D. (1958). The site of impulse initiation in a nerve cell of a crustacean stretch receptor. J. Physiol., *143*, 138-148.

Eichelberger, L., and Richter, R. B. (1944). Water, nitrogen, and electrolyte concentration in brain. J. Biol. Chem., *154*, 21-29.

Eide, E., Lundberg, A., and Voorhoeve, P. (1961). Monosynaptically evoked inhibitory post-synaptic potentials in motoneurones. Acta. physiol. scandinav., *53*, 185-195.

Elliott, K. A. C., and Florey, E. (1956). Factor I — inhibitory factor from brain. J. Neurochem., *1*, 181-191.

Elliott, K. A. C., and Jasper, H. H. (1949). Physiological salt solutions for brain surgery: studies of local pH and pial vessel reactions to buffered and unbuffered isotonic solutions. J. Neurosurg., *6*, 140-152.

Elliott, T. R. (1904). On the action of adrenalin. J. Physiol., *31*, XX-XXI.

——— (1905). The action of adrenalin. J. Physiol., *32*, 401-467.

Ellis, C. H., Thienes, C. H., and Wiersma, C. A. G. (1942). The influence of certain drugs on the crustacean nerve-muscle system. Biol. Bull., Woods Hole, *83*, 334-352.

Emmelin, N. (1960). Is there a leakage of acetylcholine from postganglionic parasympathetic nerve endings? Nature, *185*, 297-298.

Emmelin, N., and MacIntosh, F. C. (1956). The release of acetylcholine from perfused sympathetic ganglia and skeletal muscles. J. Physiol., *131*, 477-496.

Emmelin, N., and Muren, A. (1950). Acetylcholine release at parasympathetic synapses. Acta physiol. scandinav., *20*, 13-32.

Engelhart, E., and Loewi, O. (1930). Fermentative Azetylcholinspaltung im Blut und ihre Hemmung durch Physostigmin. Arch. exper. Path. u. Pharmakol., *150*, 1-13.

Erspamer, V. (1954). Il sistema cellulare enterocromaffina e l'enteramina (5-idrossitriptamina). R. C. sc. farmital., *1*, 1-193.

Evans, D. H. L., Schild, H. O., and Thesleff, S. (1958). Effects of drugs on depolarized plain muscle. J. Physiol., *143*, 474-485.

Evarts, E. V., Landau, W., Freygang, W., and Marshall, W. H. (1955). Some effects of lysergic acid diethylamide and bufotenine on electrical activity in the cat's visual system. Am. J. Physiol., *182*, 594-598.

Eyzaguirre, C., and Kuffler, S. W. (1955a). Processes of excitation in the dendrites and in the soma of single isolated sensory nerve cells of the lobster and crayfish. J. Gen. Physiol., *39*, 87-119.

——, —— (1955b). Further study of soma, dendrite, and axon excitation in single neurons. J. Gen. Physiol., *39*, 121-153.

Fadiga, E., and Brookhart, J. M. (1960). Monosynaptic activation of different portions of the motor neuron membrane. Am. J. Physiol., *198*, 693-703.

Fatt, P. (1957). Electric potentials occurring around a neurone during its antidromic activation. J. Neurophysiol., *20*, 27-60.

Fatt, P., and Katz, B. (1950). Some observations on biological noise. Nature, *166*, 597-598.

——, —— (1951). An analysis of the end-plate potential recorded with an intra-cellular electrode. J. Physiol., *115*, 320-370.

——, —— (1952). Spontaneous subthreshold activity at motor nerve endings. J. Physiol., *117*, 109-128.

Feldberg, W. (1945). Present views on the mode of action of acetylcholine in the central nervous system. Physiol. Rev., *25*, 596-642.

Feldberg, W., and Gaddum, J. H. (1934). The chemical transmitter at synapses in a sympathetic ganglion. J. Physiol., *81*, 305-319.

Feldberg, W., Harris, G. W., and Lin, R. C. Y. (1951). Observations on the presence of cholinergic and non-cholinergic neurones in the central nervous system. J. Physiol., *112*, 400-404.

Feldberg, W., and Malcolm, J. L. (1959). Experiments on the site of action of tubocurarine when applied via the cerebral ventricles. J. Physiol., *149*, 58-77.

Feldberg, W., and Sherwood, S. L. (1954a). Injections of drugs into the lateral ventricle of the cat. J. Physiol., *123*, 148-167.

——, —— (1954b). Behaviour of cats after intraventricular injections of eserine and DFP. J. Physiol., *125*, 488-500.

Feldberg, W., and Vartiainen, A. (1934). Further observations on the physiology and pharmacology of a sympathetic ganglion. J. Physiol., *83*, 103-128.

Feldberg, W., and Vogt, M. (1948). Acetylcholine synthesis in different regions of the central nervous system. J. Physiol., *107*, 372-381.

Fernandez de Molina, A., Gray, J. A. B., and Palmer, J. F. (1958). Effects of acetylcholine on the activity of the lumbosacral cord of the cat. J. Physiol., *141*, 169-176.

Fernández-Morán, H. (1955). Estudios sobre la organización submicroscópica del tálamo. Cong. latino-am. Neurocir., *6*, 599-753.

Fessard, A. (1956). Formes et charactères généraux de l'excitation neuronique. Abstr. XX internat. physiol. Cong., *1*, 35-58.

Fessard, A., and Tauc, L. (1956). Capacité, résistance et variations actives d'impédance d'un soma neuronnique. J. Physiol., Paris, *48*, 541-544.

Florey, E. (1953). Über einen nervösen Hemmungsfaktor in Gehirn und Rückenmark. Naturwissenschaften, *40*, 295-296.

—— (1954a). Über die Wirkung von 5-Oxytryptamin (Enteramin) in der Krebsschere. Ztschr. Naturf., *9b*, 540-547.

—— (1954b). An inhibitory and an excitatory factor of mammalian central nervous system, and their action on a single sensory neuron. Arch. internat. Physiol., *62*, 33-53.

—— (1955). Untersuchungen über die Impuls-Entstehung in den Streckreceptoren des Flusskrebses. Ztschr. Naturf., *10b*, 591-597.

—— (1956). The action of Factor I on certain invertebrate organs. Canad. J. Biochem. & Physiol., *34*, 669-681.

—— (1957). Further evidence for the transmitter function of Factor I. Naturwissenschaften, *44*, 424-425.

—— (1960a). Physiological evidence for naturally occurring inhibitory substances, in: *Inhibition in the Nervous System and γ-Aminobutyric Acid* (E. Roberts, ed.). Oxford, Pergamon Press, pp. 72-84.

—— (1960b). Studies on the nervous regulation of the heart beat in decapod crustacea. J. Gen. Physiol., *43*, 1061-1081.

—— (1961). Comparative physiology: transmitter substances. Ann. Rev. Physiol., *23*, 501-528.

Florey, E., and Biederman, M. A. (1960). Studies on the distribution of Factor I and acetylcholine in crustacean peripheral nerve. J. Gen. Physiol., *43*, 509-522.

Florey, E., and Chapman, D. D. (1961). The non-identity of the transmitter substance of crustacean inhibitory neurons and gamma-aminobutyric acid. Comp. Biochem. Physiol., *3*, 92-98.

Florey, E., and Florey, E. (1954). Über die mögliche Bedeutung von Enteramin (5-Oxy-Tryptamin) als nervöser Aktionssubstanz bei Cephalopoden und dekapoden Crustaceen. Ztschr. Naturf., *9b*, 58-68.

——, —— (1955). Microanatomy of the abdominal stretch receptors of the crayfish (*Astacus fluviatilis* L.). J. Gen. Physiol., *39*, 69-85.

——, —— (1958). Studies on the distribution of Factor I in mammalian brain. J. Physiol., *144*, 220-228.

Florey, E., and McLennan, H. (1955a). The release of an inhibitory substance from mammalian brain, and its effect on peripheral synaptic transmission. J. Physiol., *129*, 384-392.

——, —— (1955b). Effects of an inhibitory factor (Factor I) from brain on central synaptic transmission. J. Physiol., *130*, 446-455.

——, —— (1955c). Is ATP the sensory transmitter substance? Naturwissenschaften, *42*, 561.

——, —— (1959). The effects of Factor I and of gamma-aminobutyric acid on smooth muscle preparations. J. Physiol., *145*, 66-76.

Florey, E., and Merwin, H. J. (1961). Inhibition in molluscan hearts and the role of acetylcholine, in: *Nervous Inhibition* (E. Florey, ed.). Oxford, Pergamon Press, pp. 136-143.

Frank, K. (1959). Basic mechanisms of synaptic transmission in the central nervous system. I.R.E. Tr. Med. Electron., *ME-6*, 85-88.

Frank, K., and Fuortes, M. G. F. (1955). Potentials recorded from the spinal cord with microelectrodes. J. Physiol., *130*, 625-654.

———, ——— (1956). Unitary activity of spinal interneurones of cats. J. Physiol., *131*, 425-435.

———, ——— (1957). Presynaptic and postsynaptic inhibition of monosynaptic reflexes. Fed. Proc., *16*, 39.

Franz, J., Boissonnas, R. A., and Stürmer, E. (1961). Isolierung von Substanz P aus Pferdedarm und ihre biologische und chemische Abgrenzung gegenüber Bradykinin. Helvet. chim. acta, *44*, 881-883.

Fulton, J. F. (1921). Studies on neuromuscular transmission. I. The action of novocaine on muscle nuclei. Am. J. Physiol., *57*, 153-170.

Furchgott, R. F. (1959). The receptors for epinephrine and norepinephrine (adrenergic receptors). Pharmacol. Rev., *11*, 429-441.

——— (1960). Receptors for sympathomimetic amines, in: *Adrenergic Mechanisms* (J. R. Vane, ed.). London, Churchill, pp. 246-252.

Furshpan, E. J., and Potter, D. D. (1959). Transmission at the giant motor synapses of the crayfish. J. Physiol., *145*, 289-325.

Gaddum, J. H. (1953). Antagonism between lysergic acid diethylamide and 5-hydroxytryptamine. J. Physiol., *121*, 15P.

Gaddum, J. H., and Hameed, K. A. (1954). Drugs which antagonize 5-hydroxytryptamine. Brit. J. Pharmacol., *9*, 240-248.

Gaddum, J. H., and Vogt, M. (1956). Some central actions of 5-hydroxytryptamine and various antagonists. Brit. J. Pharmacol., *11*, 175-179.

Gaskell, W. H. (1887). On the action of muscarine upon the heart, and on the electrical changes in the non-beating cardiac muscle brought about by stimulation of the inhibitory and augmentor nerves. J. Physiol., *8*, 404-415.

Gasser, H. S., and Erlanger, J. (1922). A study of the action currents of nerve with the cathode ray oscillograph. Am. J. Physiol., *62*, 496-524.

Gertner, S. B., Paasonen, M. K., and Giarman, N. J. (1957). Presence of 5-hydroxytryptamine (serotonin) in perfusate from sympathetic ganglia. Fed. Proc., *16*, 299.

Ginsborg, B. L. (1960). Spontaneous activity in muscle fibres of the chick. J. Physiol., *150*, 707-717.

Goffart, M. (1957). Action de l'adrénaline, de la noradrénaline et de l'isopropylnoradrénaline sur la transmission synaptiques dans les ganglions du système nerveux autonome, in: *L'Adrénaline et la Noradrénaline dans la Régulation des Fonctions Homéostasiques*. Colloques Nationaux du C.N.R.S., Paris.

Goffart, M., and Perry, W. L. M. (1951). The action of adrenaline on the rate of loss of potassium ions from unfatigued striated muscle. J. Physiol., *112*, 95-101.

Granit, R., and Phillips, C. G. (1956). Excitatory and inhibitory processes acting upon individual Purkinje cells of the cerebellum in cats. J. Physiol., *133*, 520-547.

Gray, E. G. (1959). Axo-somatic and axo-dendritic synapses of the cerebral cortex: an electron microscope study. J. Anat., London, *93*, 420-433.

Grundfest, H. (1957). Electrical inexcitability of synapses and some consequences in the central nervous system. Physiol. Rev., *37*, 337-361.

——— (1961). Functional specifications for membranes in excitable cells, in: *The Regional Chemistry, Phy-*

siology and Pharmacology of the Nervous System (S. Katz, ed.). Oxford, Pergamon Press.

Haapanen, L., Kolmodin, G. M., and Skoglund, C. R. (1958). Membrane and action potentials of spinal interneurons in the cat. Acta physiol. scandinav., *43*, 315-348.

Haase, J., and van der Meulen, J. P. (1961). Die supraspinale Kontrolle der Renshaw-Zellen. Pflügers Arch. ges. Physiol., *274*, 50.

Hagiwara, S., and Tasaki, I. (1958). A study of the mechanism of impulse transmission across the giant synapse of the squid. J. Physiol., *143*, 114-137.

Hagiwara, S., Watanabe, A., and Saito, N. (1959). Potential changes in syncytial neurons of lobster cardiac ganglion. J. Neurophysiol., *22*, 554-572.

Hama, K. (1961). Some observations on the fine structure of the giant fibers of the crayfishes (*Cambarus virilis* and *Cambarus clarkii*) with special reference to the submicroscopic organization of the synapses. Anat. Rec., *141*, 275-293.

Hanström, B. (1925). Über die sogenannten intelligenzsphären des Molluskengehirns und die Innervation des Tentakels von Helix. Acta Zool., *6*, 183-215.

Harris, E. J. (1954). Ionophoresis along frog muscle. J. Physiol., *124*, 248-253.

Harris, E. J., and Hutter, O. F. (1956). The action of acetylcholine on the movement of potassium ions in the sinus venosus of the heart. J. Physiol., *133*, 58-59P.

Harris, G. W., and Holton, P. (1953). Vasodilator activity in extracts of various regions of the central nervous system. J. Physiol., *120*, 254-256.

Harris, G. W., Jacobsohn, D., and Kahlson, G. (1952). The occurrence of histamine in cerebral regions related to the hypophysis. Ciba Found. Coll. Endocrinol., *4*, 186-193.

Harvey, A. M., and MacIntosh, F. C. (1940). Calcium and synaptic transmission in a sympathetic ganglion. J. Physiol., *97*, 408-416.

Hayashi, T. (1959). The inhibitory action of β-hydroxy-γ-aminobutyric acid upon the seizure following stimulation of the motor cortex of the dog. J. Physiol., *145*, 570-578.

Hebb, C. O., and Smallman, B. N. (1956). Intracellular distribution of choline acetylase. J. Physiol., *134*, 385-392.

Hebb, C. O., and Waites, G. M. H. (1956). Choline acetylase in antero- and retrograde degeneration of a cholinergic nerve. J. Physiol., *132*, 667-671.

Hebb, D. O. (1949). *The Organization of Behavior*. New York, John Wiley and Sons, Inc., 335 pp.

Held, H. (1897). Beiträge zur Structur der Nervenzellen und ihrer Fortsätze. Arch. Anat. u. Physiol., Leipzig, pp. 204-294.

Hellauer, H. (1953). Zur Charakterisierung der Erregungssubstanz sensibler Nerven. Arch. exper. Path. u. Pharmakol., *219*, 234-241.

Hellauer, H. F., and Umrath, K. (1948). Über die Aktionssubstanz der sensiblen Nerven. Pflügers Arch. ges. Physiol., *249*, 619-630.

Hillarp, N. Å. (1946). Structure of the synapse and the peripheral innervation apparatus of the autonomic nervous system. Acta anat., Suppl., *4*, 1-153.

Hodgkin, A. L., and Horowicz, P. (1959). The influence of potassium and chloride ions on the membrane potential of single muscle fibres. J. Physiol., *148*, 127-160.

Hodgkin, A. L., and Keynes, R. D. (1953). The mobility and diffusion coefficient of potassium in giant axons from *Sepia*. J. Physiol., *119*, 513-528.

——, —— (1955). Active transport of cations in giant axons from *Sepia* and *Loligo*. J. Physiol., *128*, 28-60.

——, —— (1957). Movements of labelled calcium in squid giant axons. J. Physiol., *138*, 253-281.

Holmqvist, B., Lundberg, A., and Oscarsson, O. (1956). Functional organization of the dorsal spino-cerebellar tract in the cat. V. Further experiments on convergence of excitatory and inhibitory actions. Acta physiol. scandinav., *38*, 76-90.

Holton, F. A., and Holton, P. (1954). The capillary dilator substances in dry powders of spinal roots; a possible role of adenosine triphosphate in chemical transmission from nerve endings. J. Physiol., *126*, 124-140.

Holton, P. (1959a). The liberation of adenosine triphosphate on antidromic stimulation of sensory nerves. J. Physiol., *145*, 494-504.

—— (1959b). Further observations on substance P in degenerating nerve. J. Physiol., *149*, 35-36P.

Holton, P., and Perry, W. L. M. (1951). On the transmitter responsible for antidromic vasodilatation in the rabbit's ear. J. Physiol., *114*, 240-251.

Holtz, P. (1960). Aminosäurendecarboxylasen des Nervengewebes. Psychiat. Neurol., Basel, *140*, 175-189.

Holtz, P., Credner, K., and Kroneberg, G. (1947). Über das sympathicomimetische pressorische Prinzip des Harns ("Urosympathin"). Arch. exper. Path. u. Pharmakol., *204*, 228-243.

Holzbauer, M., and Vogt, M. (1956). Depression by reserpine of the noradrenaline concentration of the hypothalamus of the cat. J. Neurochem., *1*, 8-11.

Honour, A. J., and McLennan, H. (1960). The effects of γ-aminobutyric acid and other compounds on structures of the mammalian nervous system which are inhibited by Factor I. J. Physiol., *150*, 306-318.

Horstmann, E. (1957). Ergebnisse und Probleme der Morphologie interneuronaler Synapsen. Deutsche med. Wchnschr., *18*, 733-735.

Hosein, E., and McLennan, H. (1959). Pharmacological actions of γ-butyrobetaine. Nature, *183*, 328-329.

Hosein, E. A., Proulx, P., and Ara, R. (1962). Substances with acetylcholine activity in normal rat brain. Biochem. J., *83*, 341-346.

Howell, W. H., and Duke, W. W. (1908). The effect of vagus inhibition on the output of potassium from the heart. Am. J. Physiol., *21*, 51-63.

Hoyle, G., and Lowy, J. (1956). The paradox of *Mytilus* muscle. A new interpretation. J. exper. Biol., *33*, 295-310.

Hoyle, G., and Wiersma, C. A. G. (1958a). Excitation at neuromuscular junctions in Crustacea. J. Physiol., *143*, 403-425.

——, —— (1958b). Inhibition at neuromuscular junctions in Crustacea. J. Physiol., *143*, 426-440.

Hubbard, J. I. (1961). The effect of calcium and magnesium on the spontaneous release of transmitter from mammalian motor nerve endings. J. Physiol., *159*, 507-517.

Hubbard, J. I., and Willis, W. D. (1962). Mobilization of transmitter by hyperpolarization. Nature, *193*, 174-175.

Hunt, C. C., and Kuno, M. (1959). Properties of spinal interneurones. J. Physiol., *147*, 346-363.

Hunt, R. (1901). Further observations on the blood-pressure-lowering bodies in extracts of the suprarenal gland. Am. J. Physiol., *5*, vi-vii.

Hunt, R., and Taveau, R. de M. (1906). On the physiological action of certain cholin derivatives and new methods for detecting cholin. Brit. M. J., *2*, 1788-1791.

Hutter, O. F. (1961). Ion movements during vagus inhibition of the heart, in: *Nervous Inhibition* (E. Florey, ed.). Oxford, Pergamon Press, pp. 114-123.

Hutter, O. F., and Kostial, K. (1955). The relationship of sodium ions to the release of acetylcholine. J. Physiol., *129*, 159-166.

Hutter, O. F., and Trautwein, W. (1956). Vagal and sympathetic effects on the pacemaker fibers in the sinus venosus of the heart. J. Gen. Physiol., *39*, 715-733.

Inouye, A., and Kataoka, K. (1962). Sub-cellular distribution of the substance P in the nervous tissues. Nature, *193*, 585.

Ito, M. (1957). The electrical activity of spinal ganglion cells investigated with intracellular microelectrodes. Jap. J. Physiol., *7*, 297-323.

Ivy, A. C., Goetzl, F. R., Harris, S. C., and Burrill, D. Y. (1944). The analgesic effect of intracarotid and intravenous injection of epinephrine in dogs and of subcutaneous injection in man. Quart. Bull. Northwestern Univ. M. School, *18*, 298-306.

Jaeger, C. P. (1961). Physiology of Mollusca. I. Action of acetylcholine on the heart of *Strophocheilos oblongus*. Comp. Biochem. Physiol., *4*, 30-32.

Johnson, G. E. (1924). Giant nerve fibres in crustaceans with special reference to *Cambarus* and *Palaemonetes*. J. Comp. Neurol., *36*, 323-373.

Jolly, W. A. (1910). The time relations of the knee-jerk and simple reflexes. Quart. J. exper. Physiol., *4*, 67-87.

Kandel, E. R., Spencer, W. A., and Brinley, F. J., Jr. (1961). Electrophysiology of hippocampal neurons. I. Sequential invasion and synaptic organization. J. Neurophysiol., *24*, 225-242.

Katz, B. (1958). Microphysiology of the neuro-muscular junction. Bull. Johns Hopkins Hosp., *102*, 275-312.

Katz, B., and Miledi, R. (1962). The nature of spontaneous synaptic potentials in motoneurones of the frog. J. Physiol., *162*, 51-52P.

Kewitz, H. (1954). Zur Bedeutung des Acetylcholins als Überträgersubstanz sympathischer Ganglien. Arch. exper. Path. u. Pharmakol., *222*, 323-329.

—— (1959). Nachweis von 4-Amino-n-butyrylcholin im Warmblütergehirn. Arch. exper. Path. u. Pharmakol., *237*, 308-318.

Kewitz, H., and Reinert, H. (1954a). Wirkung verschiedener Sympathomimetica auf die chemisch und elektrisch ausgelöste Erregung des oberen Halsganglions. Arch. exper. Path. u. Pharmakol., *222*, 311-314.

——, —— (1954b). Differenzierung zwischen der Acetylcholinerregung und der Überträgerfunktion sympathischer Ganglien mit Hilfe verschieden zusammengesetzter Durchströmungsflüssigkeiten. Arch. exper. Path. u. Pharmakol., *222*, 315-322.

Keynes, R. D., and Lewis, P. R. (1951). The sodium and potassium content of cephalopod nerve fibres. J. Physiol., *114*, 151-182.

Koelle, G. B. (1954). The histochemical localization of cholinesterases in the central nervous system of the rat. J. Comp. Neurol., *100*, 211-235.

—— (1959). Possible mechanisms for the termination of the physiological actions of catecholamines. Pharmacol. Rev., 11, 381-386.

—— (1962). A new general concept of the neurohumoral functions of acetylcholine and acetylcholinesterase. J. Pharm. Pharmacol., 14, 65-90.

Koelle, G. B., and Friedenwald, J. S. (1949). A histochemical method for locating cholinesterase activity. Proc. Soc. exper. Biol., N.Y., 70, 617-622.

Koelle, W. A., and Koelle, G. B. (1959). The localization of external or functional acetylcholinesterase at the synapses of autonomic ganglia. J. Pharmacol., 126, 1-8.

Kolmodin, G. M., and Skoglund, C. R. (1958). Slow membrane potential changes accompanying excitation and inhibition in spinal moto- and interneurons in the cat during natural activation. Acta physiol. scandinav., 44, 11-54.

Konzett, H. (1950). Sympathomimetica und Sympatholytica am isoliert durchströmten Ganglion cervicale superius der Katze. Helvet. physiol. acta, 8, 245-258.

—— (1952). The effect of histamine on an isolated sympathetic ganglion. J. Mt. Sinai Hosp., 19, 149-153.

Kostiuk, P. G. (1960). Electrophysiological characteristics of individual spinal cord neurons. Sechenov J. Physiol., London, 46, 10-22.

Kravitz, E. A., Potter, D. D., and van Gelder, N. M. (1962a). Gamma-aminobutyric acid and other blocking substances extracted from crab muscle. Nature, 194, 382-383.

——, ——, —— (1962b). Gamma-aminobutyric acid distribution in the lobster nervous system: CNS, peripheral nerves and isolated motor and inhibitory axons. Biochem. Biophys. Res. Comm., 7, 231-236.

Krnjević, K., and Miledi, R. (1958a). Failure of neuromuscular propagation in rats. J. Physiol., 140, 440-461.

——, —— (1958b). Some effects produced by adrenaline upon neuromuscular propagation in rats. J. Physiol., 141, 291-304.

Kuffler, S. W., and Edwards, C. (1958). Mechanism of gamma aminobutyric acid (GABA) action and its relation to synaptic inhibition. J. Neurophysiol., 21, 589-610.

Kuffler, S. W., and Eyzaguirre, C. (1955). Synaptic inhibition in an isolated nerve cell. J. Gen. Physiol., 39, 155-184.

Kuno, M. (1959). Excitability following antidromic activation in spinal motoneurones supplying red muscles. J. Physiol., 149, 374-393.

Kuntzman, R., Shore, P. A., Bogdanski, D., and Brodie, B. B. (1961). Microanalytical procedures for fluorometric assay of brain DOPA-5-HTP decarboxylase, norepinephrine and serotonin, and a detailed mapping of decarboxylase activity in brain. J. Neurochem., 6, 226-232.

Kuriaki, K., Yakushiji, T., Noro, T., Shimizu, T., and Saji, Sh. (1958). Gamma-aminobutyrylcholine. Nature, 181, 1336-1337.

Kwiatowski, H. (1943). Histamine in nervous tissue. J. Physiol., 102, 32-41.

Langley, J. N. (1901). Observations on the physiological action of extracts of the supra-renal bodies. J. Physiol., 27, 237-256.

—— (1923). Antidromic action. Part II. Stimulation of the peripheral nerves of the cat's hind foot. J. Physiol., 58, 49-69.

Lapique, L. (1926). "L'Excitabilité en Fonction du Temps; La Chronaxie, sa Signification et sa Mesure." Paris, Presses Universitaires de France.

Lechner, H., and Lembeck, F. (1958). Einfluss der Substanz P auf die elektrische Aktivität des Gehirns. Arch. exper. Path. u. Pharmakol., 234, 419-425.

Lembeck, F. (1953). Zur Frage der zentralen Übertragung afferenter Impulse. III Mitteilung. Das Vorkommen und die Bedeutung der Substanz P in den dorsalen Wurzeln des Rückenmarks. Arch. exper. Path. u. Pharmakol., 219, 197-213.

Lewandowsky, M. (1899). Über die Wirkung des Nebennierenextractes auf die glatten Muskeln, im Besonderen des Auges. Arch. Anat. u. Physiol., Leipzig, pp. 360-366.

Li, C. L. (1959). Cortical intracellular potentials and their responses to strychnine. J. Neurophysiol., 22, 436-450.

Li, C. L., Chou, S. N., and Howard, S. Y. (1961). Basic mechanisms of single cell discharge in the cerebral cortex. Epilepsia, 2, 13-21.

Li, C. L., Cullen, C., and Jasper, H. (1956). Laminar microelectrode studies of specific somato-sensory cortical potentials. J. Neurophysiol., 19, 111-130.

Li, C. L., Ortiz-Galvin, A., Chou, S. N., and Howard, S. Y. (1960). Cortical intracellular potentials in response to stimulation of lateral geniculate body. J. Neurophysiol., 23, 592-601.

Liddell, E. G. T., and Sherrington, C. (1925). Further observations on myotatic reflexes. Proc. Roy. Soc. London B:97, 267-283.

Liley, A. W. (1956a). An investigation of spontaneous activity at the neuromuscular junction of the rat. J. Physiol., 132, 650-666.

—— (1956b). The effects of presynaptic polarization on the spontaneous activity at the mammalian neuromuscular junction. J. Physiol., 134, 427-443.

Lilleheil, G., and Naess, K. (1960). Presynaptic effect of D-tubocurarine. Experientia, 16, 550-551.

——, —— (1961). A presynaptic effect of d-tubocurarine in the neuromuscular junction. Acta physiol. scandinav., 52, 120-136.

Ling, G., and Gerard, R. W. (1949). The normal membrane potential of frog sartorius fibers. J. Cell. & Comp. Physiol., 34, 383-396.

Ling, G. M., and Foulks, J. G. (1959). A suitable preparation for pharmacological analysis of EEG "activation." Proc. Soc. exper. Biol., N.Y., 101, 429-432.

Lissák, K., and Endröczi, E. (1956). Presence in nerve tissue of substances inhibiting nervous function and blocking the action of chemical mediators. Acta physiol. acad. sc. Hungary, 9, 111-121.

Lissák, K., Endröczi, E., and Fábián, I. (1957). Further studies on the effect of the humoral inhibitory factor. Acta physiol. acad. sc. Hungary, 11, 376-383.

Lissák, K., Endröczi, E., and Vincze, E. (1961). Further observations concerning the inhibitory substance extracted from brain, in: Nervous Inhibition (E. Florey, ed.). Oxford, Pergamon Press, pp. 369-375.

Lloyd, D. P. C. (1941). A direct central inhibitory action of dromically conducted impulses. J. Neurophysiol., 4, 184-190.

—— (1943). Neuron patterns controlling transmission of ipsilateral hind limb reflexes in cat. J. Neurophysiol., 6, 293-315.

—— (1946a). Facilitation and inhibition of spinal motoneurons. J. Neurophysiol., 9, 421-438.

—— (1946b). Integrative pattern of excitation and inhibition in two-neuron reflex arc. J. Neurophysiol., 9, 439-444.

—— (1957). Monosynaptic reflex response of individual motoneurons as a function of frequency. J. Gen. Physiol., 40, 435-450.

Lloyd, D. P. C., and Wilson, V. J. (1957). Reflex depression in rhythmically active monosynaptic reflex pathways. J. Gen. Physiol., 40, 409-426.

Loewi, O. (1921). Über humorale Übertragbarkeit der Herznervenwirkung. I. Mitteilung. Pflügers Arch. ges. Physiol., 189, 239-242.

—— (1922). Über humorale Übertragbarkeit der Herznervenwirkung. II. Mitteilung. Pflügers Arch. ges. Physiol., 193, 201-213.

Loewi, O., and Hellauer, H. (1938). Über das Acetylcholin in peripheren Nerven. Pflügers Arch. ges. Physiol., 240, 769-775.

Loewi, O., and Navratil, E. (1926a). Über humorale Übertragbarkeit der Herznervenwirkung. X. Mitteilung. Über das Schicksal des Vagusstoffs. Pflügers Arch. ges. Physiol., 214, 678-688.

——, —— (1926b). Über humorale Übertragbarkeit der Herznervenwirkung. XI. Mitteilung. Über den Mechanismus der Vaguswirkung von Physostigmin und Ergotamin. Pflügers Arch. ges. Physiol., 214, 689-696.

Lowe, I. P., Robins, E., and Eyerman, G. S. (1958). The fluorimetric measurement of glutamic decarboxylase and its distribution in brain. J. Neurochem., 3, 8-18.

Lundberg, A. (1952). Adrenaline and transmission in the sympathetic ganglion of the cat. Acta physiol. scandinav., 26, 252-263.

MacIntosh, F. C. (1941). The distribution of acetylcholine in the peripheral and the central nervous system. J. Physiol., 99, 436-442.

—— (1959). Formation, storage, and release of acetylcholine at nerve endings. Canad. J. Biochem. Physiol., 37, 343-356.

MacIntosh, F. C., Birks, R. I., and Sastry, P. B. (1956). Pharmacological inhibition of acetylcholine synthesis. Nature, 178, 1181.

——, ——, —— (1958). Mode of action of an inhibitor of acetylcholine synthesis. Neurology, 8, Suppl. 1, 90-91.

McGeer, E. G., McGeer, P. L., and McLennan, H. (1961). The inhibitory action of 3-hydroxytyramine, gamma-aminobutyric acid (GABA) and some other compounds towards the crayfish stretch receptor neuron. J. Neurochem., 8, 36-49.

McLennan, H. (1957a). The diffusion of potassium, sodium, sucrose and inulin in the extracellular space of mammalian tissues. Biochem. et Biophys. acta, 24, 1-8.

—— (1957b). A comparison of some physiological properties of an inhibitory factor from brain (Factor I) and of γ-aminobutyric acid and related compounds. J. Physiol., 139, 79-86.

—— (1960a). The fractionation and purification of Factor I. J. Physiol., 151, 31-39.

—— (1960b). Evidence for the presence of an inhibitory transmitter substance in Factor I extracts. J. Physiol., 153, 55-56P.

—— (1961a). The effect of some catecholamines upon a monosynaptic reflex pathway in the spinal cord. J. Physiol., 158, 411-425.

—— (1961b). Inhibitory transmitters—a review, in: Nervous Inhibition (E. Florey, ed.). Oxford, Pergamon Press, pp. 350-368.

—— (1962). On the action of 3-hydroxytyramine and dichloroisopropylnoradrenaline on spinal reflexes. Experientia, 18, 278-279.

McLennan, H., and Hagen, B. A. (1962). On the response of the stretch receptor neurones of crayfish to catecholamines and other compounds. Comp. Biochem. Physiol., in the press.

Machne, X., Fadiga, E., and Brookhart, J. M. (1959). Antidromic and synaptic activation of frog motor neurons. J. Neurophysiol., 22, 483-503.

Magendie, F. (1807). Examen de l'action de quelques végetaux sur la moelle epinière. Paris.

Magnus, R., and Wolf, C. G. L. (1913). Weitere Mitteilungen über den Einfluss der Kopfstellung auf der Gliedertonus. Pflügers Arch. ges. Physiol., 149, 447-461.

Malméjac, J. (1955). Action of adrenaline on synaptic transmission and on adrenal medullary secretion. J. Physiol., 130, 497-512.

Mann, P. J. G., Tennenbaum, M., and Quastel, J. H. (1938). On the mechanism of acetylcholine formation in brain in vitro. Biochem. J., 32, 243-261.

Marrazzi, A. S. (1939). Electrical studies on the pharmacology of autonomic synapses. II. The action of a sympathomimetic drug (epinephrine) on sympathetic ganglia. J. Pharmacol., 65, 395-404.

—— (1953). Quoted in Page, I. H., and McCubbin, J. W. (1953): The variable arterial pressure response to serotonin in laboratory animals and man. Circulation Res., 1, 354-362.

Martin, A. R., and Orkand, R. K. (1961). Postsynaptic effects of HC-3 at the neuromuscular junction of the frog. Canad. J. Biochem. Physiol., 39, 343-349.

Masland, R. L., and Wigton, R. S. (1940). Nerve activity accompanying fasiculation produced by prostigmin. J. Neurophysiol., 3, 269-275.

Matsumara, M., and Koelle, G. B. (1961). The nature of synaptic transmission in the superior cervical ganglion following reinnervation by the afferent vagus. J. Pharmacol., 134, 28-46.

Matteucci, C. (1842). Sur une phénomène électrique produite par les muscles en contraction. C.R. Acad. Sc., Paris, 14, 797.

Matthes, K. (1930). The action of blood on acetylcholine. J. Physiol., 70, 338-348.

Matthews, R. J. (1956). The effect of epinephrine, levarterenol, and DL-isoproterenol on transmission in the superior cervical ganglion. J. Pharmacol., 116, 433-443.

Matthews, R. J., and Roberts, B. J. (1961). The effect of γ-aminobutyric acid on synaptic transmission in autonomic ganglia. J. Pharmacol., 132, 19-22.

Muscholl, E., and Vogt, M. (1958). The action of reserpine on the peripheral sympathetic system. J. Physiol., 141, 132-155.

Nachmansohn, D. (1940). On the physiological significance of choline esterase. Yale J. Biol. & Med., 12, 565-589.

Nachmansohn, D., and Machado, A. L. (1943). The formation of acetylcholine. A new enzyme: "choline acetylase." J. Neurophysiol., 6, 397-403.

Nishi, S., and Koketsu, K. (1960). Electrical properties and activities of single sympathetic neurons in frogs. J. Cell. & Comp. Physiol., 55, 15-30.

Ogston, A. G. (1955). Removal of acetylcholine from a limited volume by diffusion. J. Physiol., *128*, 222-223.

Ohara, K., Sano, I., Koizumi, H., and Nishinuma, K. (1959). Free β-hydroxy-γ-aminobutyric acid in brain. Science, *129*, 1225-1226.

Okinaka, S., and Yoshikawa, M. (1955). Zur Klinik der Cholinesterase. München med. Wchnschr., *97*, 1072-1079.

Okinaka, S., Yoshikawa, M., Uono, M., Muro, T., Mozai, T., Igata, A., Tanabe, H., Ueda, S., and Tomonaga, M. (1961). Distribution of cholinesterase activity in the human cerebral cortex. Am. J. Phys. Med., *40*, 135-145.

Paasonen, M. K., and Vogt, M. (1956). The effect of drugs on the amounts of substance P and 5-hydroxytryptamine in mammalian brain. J. Physiol., *131*, 617-626.

Page, I. H. (1958). Serotonin (5-hydroxytryptamine); the last four years. Physiol. Rev., *38*, 277-335.

Palade, G. E. (1956). The endoplasmic reticulum. J. Biophys. Biochem. Cytol., *2*, Suppl., 85-98.

Palay, S. L. (1954). Electron microscope study of the cytoplasm of neurons. Anat. Rec., *118*, 336.

——— (1956). Synapses in the central nervous system. J. Biophys. Biochem. Cytol., *2*, Suppl., 193-202.

Pappius, H. M., and Elliott, K. A. C. (1956). Factors affecting the potassium content of incubated brain slices. Canad. J. Biochem. Physiol., *34*, 1053-1067.

Pascoe, J. E. (1956). The effects of acetylcholine and other drugs on the isolated superior cervical ganglion. J. Physiol., *132*, 242-255.

Pataky, I., and Pfeifer, A. K. (1955). Physiological significance of the acetylcholine blocking agent in the central nervous system. Acta physiol. acad. sc. Hungary, *8*, 221-229.

Paton, W. D. M., and Perry, W. L. M. (1953). The relationship between depolarization and block in the cat's superior cervical ganglion. J. Physiol., *119*, 43-57.

Pernow, B. (1953). Studies on substance P—purification, occurrence and biological actions. Acta physiol. scandinav., *29*, Suppl., 105.

——— (1955). The distribution and properties of substance P, in: *Polypeptides Which Stimulate Plain Muscle*, (J. H. Gaddum, ed.). Edinburgh, E. & S. Livingstone, Ltd., pp. 28-38.

Perry, W. L. M., and Talesnik, J. (1953). The role of acetylcholine in synaptic transmission at parasympathetic ganglia. J. Physiol., *119*, 455-469.

Peterson, R. P., and Pepe, F. A. (1961). The fine structure of inhibitory synapses in the crayfish. J. Biophys. Biochem. Cytol., *11*, 157-169.

Pfeifer, A. K., and Pataky, I. (1955). Acetylcholine blocking agent in the central nervous system. Acta physiol. acad. sc. Hungary, *8*, 209-219.

Phillips, C. G. (1956). Intracellular records from Betz cells in the cat. Quart. J. Exper. Physiol., *41*, 58-69.

——— (1959). Actions of antidromic pyramidal volleys on single Betz cells in the cat. Quart. J. Exper. Physiol., *44*, 1-25.

Powell, C. E., and Slater, I. H. (1958). Blocking of inhibitory adrenergic receptors by a dichloro analog of isoproterenol. J. Pharmacol., *122*, 480-488.

Preston, J. B., and Whitlock, D. G. (1960). Precentral facilitation and inhibition of spinal motoneurons. J. Neurophysiol., *23*, 154-170.

———, ——— (1961). Intracellular potentials recorded from motoneurons following precentral gyrus stimulation in primate. J. Neurophysiol., *24*, 91-100.

Prosser, C. L. (1940). Acetylcholine and nervous inhibition in the heart of Venus mercenaria. Biol. Bull., Woods Hole, *78*, 92-102.

Purpura, D. P. (1960). Pharmacological actions of ω-amino acid drugs on different cortical synaptic organizations, in: *Inhibition in the Nervous System and γ-Aminobutyric Acid* (E. Roberts, ed.). Oxford, Pergamon Press, pp. 495-514.

Purpura, D. P., Girado, M., Smith, T. G., Callan, D. A., and Grundfest, H. (1959). Structure-activity determinants of pharmacological effects of amino acids and related compounds on central synapses. J. Neurochem., *3*, 238-268.

Purpura, D. P., and Grundfest, H. (1956). Nature of dendritic potentials and synaptic mechanisms in cerebral cortex of cat. J. Neurophysiol., *19*, 573-595.

Quastel, D. M. J., and Birks, R. I. (1962). Effects of sodium ions on acetylcholine metabolism in a sympathetic ganglion. Abstr. 5th Meet. Canad. Fed. Biol. Sc., p. 64.

Quastel, J. H., Tennenbaum, M., and Wheatley, A. H. M. (1936). Choline ester formation in, and choline esterase activities of, tissues *in vitro*. Biochem. J., *30*, 1668-1681.

Rall, W. (1959). Branching dendritic trees and motoneuron membrane resistivity. Exper. Neurol., *1*, 491-527.

——— (1960). Membrane potential transients and membrane time constant of motoneurons. Exper. Neurol., *2*, 503-532.

——— (1962). Electrophysiology of a dendritic neuron model. Biophys. J., *2*, Suppl., 145-167.

Rall, T. W., and Sutherland, E. W. (1959). Action of epinephrine and norepinephrine in broken cell preparations. Pharmacol. Rev., *11*, 464-465.

Ranvier, L. (1874). De quelques faits relatifs à l'histologie et à la physiologie des muscles striés. Arch. physiol. norm. et path., *6*, 1-15.

Rech, R. H., and Domino, E. F. (1960). Effects of gamma-aminobutyric acid on chemically- and electrically-evoked activity in the isolated cerebral cortex of the dog. J. Pharmacol., *130*, 59-67.

Renshaw, B. (1941). Influence of discharge of motoneurons upon excitation of neighboring motoneurons. J. Neurophysiol., *4*, 167-183.

——— (1942). Reflex discharge in branches of the crural nerve. J. Neurophysiol., *5*, 487-498.

——— (1946). Central effects of centripetal impulses in axons of spinal ventral roots. J. Neurophysiol., *9*, 191-204.

Richardson, K. C. (1958). Electronmicroscopic observations on Auerbach's plexus in the rabbit, with special reference to the problem of smooth muscle innervation. Am. J. Anat., *103*, 99-135.

Robertson, J. D. (1953). Ultrastructure of two invertebrate synapses. Proc. Soc. Exper. Biol., N.Y., *82*, 219-223.

——— (1955). Recent electron microscope observations on the ultrastructure of the crayfish median-to-motor giant synapse. Exper. Cell Res., *8*, 226-229.

——— (1956). The ultrastructure of a reptilian myoneural junction. J. Biophys. Biochem. Cytol., *2*, 381-394.

——— (1957). The ultrastructure of nodes of Ranvier in frog nerve fibres. J. Physiol., *137*, 8-9P.

Robinson, F., and Hughes, R. A. (1951). Effects of adenine compounds on electrocortical activity. J. Neurophysiol., 14, 387-398.

Romanowski, W. (1962). Analiza mechanizmu hipotensyjnego dzialania kwasu γ-aminomaslowego. Acta physiol. polon., 13, 57-76.

Romanowski, W., Lenartowicz, P., and Janczarski, I. (1957). Examination of the effect on the heart activity of a brain extract obtained by the Florey method. Bull. acad. polon. sc., 5, 271-276.

Rose, J. E., Malis, L. E., Kruger, L., and Baker, C. P. (1960). Effects of heavy, ionizing, monoenergetic particles on the cerebral cortex. II. J. Comp. Neurol., 115, 243-255.

Rothballer, A. B. (1959). The effects of catecholamines on the central nervous system. Pharmacol. Rev., 11, 494-547.

Sato, M., and Austin, G. (1961). Intracellular potentials of mammalian dorsal root ganglion cells. J. Neurophysiol., 24, 569-582.

Sawa, M., Maruyama, N., Kaji, S., and Hanai, T. (1960). Actions of stimulation of medullary pyramid on single neurons in cat's motor cortex. Folia psychiat. neurol. jap., 14, 316-346.

Schaefer, H., and Haass, P. (1939). Über einen lokalen Erregungsstrom an der motorischen Endplatte. Pflügers Arch. ges. Physiol., 242, 364-381.

Schäfer, E. A. (1900). The nerve cell, in: Text Book of Physiology. Edinburgh, Young J. Pentland.

Schueler, F. W. (1955). A new group of respiratory paralyzants. I. The "hemicholiniums." J. Pharmacol., 115, 127-143.

Schümann, H. J. (1958). Über den Noradrenalin- und ATP-Gehalt sympathischer Nerven. Arch. exper. Path. u. Pharmakol., 233, 296-300.

Schweitzer, A., and Wright, S. (1937). The action of adrenaline on the knee jerk. J. Physiol., 88, 476-491.

Sechenov, I. M. (1863). Note sur les moderateurs reflexes dans le cerveau de la grenouille. C.R. Acad. Sc., Paris, 56, 50-53.

Sherrington, C. S. (1897). The central nervous system and its instruments, in: Sir Michael Foster's A Text Book of Physiology, 7th ed., London, Macmillan and Co., Ltd.

—— (1905). On reciprocal innervation of antagonistic muscles. Proc. Roy. Soc. London B:76, 269-297.

—— (1906). The Integrative Action of the Nervous System. New York, Charles Scribner's Sons.

Sherwood, S. L. (1952). Intraventricular medication in catatonic stupor. Brain, 75, 68-75.

Sigg, E., Ochs, S., and Gerard, R. W. (1955). Effects of the medullary hormones on the somatic nervous system in the cat. Am. J. Physiol., 183, 419-426.

Skoglund, C. R. (1961). Influence of noradrenaline on spinal interneuron activity. Acta physiol. scandinav., 51, 142-149.

Sprague, J. M. (1958). The distribution of dorsal root fibres on motor cells in the lumbosacral spinal cord of the cat, and the site of excitatory and inhibitory terminals in monosynaptic pathways. Proc. Roy. Soc. London B:149, 534-556.

Staub, H. (1946). Die Adrenalin-Histamin-Regulation, gleichzeitig Beitrag zum Antistimmechanismus. Helvet. physiol. acta, 4, 539-550.

Stolz, F. (1904). Über Adrenalin und Alkylaminoacetobrenzcatechin. Ber. deutsch. chem. Gesellsch., 37, 4149-4154.

Straughan, D. W. (1961). The action of procaine at the neuromuscular junction. J. Pharm. & Pharmacol., 13, 49-52.

Stricker, S. (1876). Untersuchungen über die Gefässnerven-Wurzeln des Ischiadicus. S.B. Akad. Wiss., Wien, 74, 173-185.

Sutherland, E. W., and Rall, T. W. (1960). The relation of adenosine-3′, 5′-phosphate and phosphorylase to the actions of catecholamines and other hormones. Pharmacol. Rev., 12, 265-299.

Szentágothai, J. (1951). Short propriospinal neurones and intrinsic connections of the spinal gray matter. Acta morphol. acad. sc. Hungary, 1, 81-94.

—— (1958). The anatomical basis of synaptic transmission of excitation and inhibition in motoneurons. Acta morphol. acad. sc. Hungary, 8, 287-309.

Takahashi, H., Nagashima, N., and Koshino, C. (1958). Effect of γ-aminobutyrylcholine upon the electrical activity of the cerebral cortex. Nature, 182, 1443-1444.

Takeuchi, A. (1959). Neuromuscular transmission of fish skeletal muscles investigated with intracellular microelectrode. J. Cell. & Comp. Physiol., 54, 211-221.

Takeuchi, A., and Takeuchi, N. (1959). Active phase of frog's end-plate potential. J. Neurophysiol., 22, 395-411.

——, —— (1960). On the permeability of end-plate membrane during the action of transmitter. J. Physiol., 154, 52-67.

Tauc, L. (1958). Processus post-synaptique d'excitation et d'inhibition dans le soma neuronique de l'Aplysie et de l'Escargot. Arch. ital. biol., 96, 78-110.

—— (1959). Interaction non synaptique entre deux neurones adjacents du ganglion abdominal de l'Aplysie. C.R. acad. sc., Paris, 248, 1857-1859.

—— (1960a). Maintien de la transmission synaptique dans le neurone géant d'Aplysie sans activation du soma ou en l'absence du soma. C.R. acad. sc., Paris, 250, 1560-1562.

—— (1960b). The site of origin of the efferent action potentials in the giant nerve cell of Aplysia. J. Physiol., 152, 36-37P.

—— (1960c). Evidence of synaptic inhibitory actions not conveyed by inhibitory post-synaptic potentials, in: Inhibitions of the Nervous System and γ-Aminobutyric Acid (E. Roberts, ed.). Oxford, Pergamon Press, pp. 85-89.

Tauc, L., and Gerschenfeld, H. (1960). L'acétylcholine comme transmetteur possible de l'inhibition synaptique chez l'Aplysie. C.R. acad. sc., Paris, 251, 3076-3078.

——, —— (1962). A cholinergic mechanism of inhibitory synaptic transmission in a molluscan nervous system. J. Neurophysiol., 25, 236-262.

ten Cate, J., Boeles, J. T. F., and Biersteker, P. A. (1959). The action of adrenaline and nor-adrenaline on the knee-jerk. Arch. internat. physiol., 67, 468-488.

Terzuolo, C., and Araki, T. (1961). Unpublished observations, quoted in Eccles (1961b).

Thesleff, S. (1960). Supersensitivity of skeletal muscle produced by botulinum toxin. J. Physiol., 151, 598-607.

Thies, R. E., and Brooks, V. B. (1961). Postsynaptic neuromuscular block produced by hemicholinium no. 3. Fed. Proc., 20, 569-578.

Tissot, R. (1961). Monoamines et système nerveux central. L'encéphale, 50, 105-179.

Trautwein, W., Kuffler, S. W., and Edwards, C. (1956). Changes in membrane characteristics of heart muscle during inhibition. J. Gen. Physiol., 40, 135-145.

Trendelenburg, U. (1957). The action of histamine, pilocarpine and 5-hydroxytryptamine on transmission through the superior cervical ganglion. J. Physiol., 135, 66-72.

Twarog, B. M. (1960). Effects of acetylcholine and 5-hydroxytryptamine on the contraction of a molluscan smooth muscle. J. Physiol., 152, 236-242.

Twarog, B. M., and Page, I. H. (1953). Serotonin content of some mammalian tissues and urine and a method for its determination. Am. J. Physiol., 175, 157-161.

Umrath, K. (1953). Über die fermentative Verwandlung von Substanz P aus sensiblen Neuronen in die Erregungssubstanz der sensiblen Nerven. Pflügers Arch. ges. Physiol., 258, 230-242.

——— (1961). The relation of substance P to neurotransmitter substances, in: Symposium on Substance P (P. Stern, ed.). Sarajevo, Scientific Society of Bosnia and Herzegovina, pp. 23-27.

van Andel, H., and Ernst, A. M. (1961). Tryptamin-Katatonie, eine cholinergische Hypofunktion im zentralen Nervensystem. Psychopharmacologia, 2, 461-466.

van der Kloot, W. G. (1960). Factor S—a substance which excites crustacean muscle. J. Neurochem., 5, 245-252.

van der Loos, H. (1960). On dendro-dendritic junctions in the cerebral cortex, in: Structure and Function of the Cerebral Cortex (D. B. Tower and J. P. Schadé, eds.). Amsterdam, Elsevier, pp. 36-42.

Vane, J. R., ed. (1960). Adrenergic Mechanisms. London, Churchill.

Vane, J. R., Collier, H. O. J., Corne, S. J., Marley, E., and Bradley, P. B. (1961). Tryptamine receptors in the central nervous system. Nature, 191, 1068-1069.

Varga, F., Kövér, A., Kovács, T., and Hetényi, E. (1957). Changes in cholinesterase activity of striated muscle after denervation. Acta physiol. acad. sc. Hungary, 11, 235-242.

Vereshchagin, S. M., Sytinskii, I. A., and Tyshchenko, V. P. (1961). Effect of beta-oxy-gamma-aminobutyric acid on the bioelectric activity of the ganglia of an isolated neural chain of Lepidoptera. C.R. Acad. Sc. U.R.S.S., 138, 722-724.

Vogt, M. (1954). The concentration of sympathin in different parts of the central nervous system under normal conditions and after administration of drugs. J. Physiol., 123, 451-481.

Volkmann, A. W. (1838). Über Reflexbewegungen. Arch. Anat. Physiol. u. wissensch. Med., Berlin, pp. 15-44.

von Brücke, F. Th. (1937). The cholinesterase in sympathetic ganglia. J. Physiol., 89, 429-437.

von Euler, U. S. (1936). Untersuchungen über Substanz P, die atropinfeste, darmerregende und gefässerweiternde Substanz aus Darm und Hirn. Arch. exper. Path. u. Pharmakol., 181, 181-197.

——— (1948). Identification of the sympathomimetic ergone in adrenergic nerves of cattle (sympathin N) with laevo-noradrenaline. Acta physiol. scandinav., 16, 63-74.

——— (1955). Noradrenaline. Springfield, Charles C Thomas.

von Euler, U. S., and Gaddum, J. H. (1931). An unidentified depressor substance in certain tissue extracts. J. Physiol., 72, 74-87.

von Euler, U. S., and Pernow, B. (1956). Neurotropic effects of substance P. Acta physiol. scandinav., 36, 265-275.

von Euler, U. S., and Purkhold, A. (1951). Effect of sympathetic denervation on the noradrenaline and adrenaline content of the spleen, kidney, and salivary glands in the sheep. Acta physiol. scandinav., 24, 212-217.

von Lenhossék, M. (1890). Über Nervenfasern in den hinteren Wurzeln, welche aus dem Vorderhorn entspringen. Anat. Anz., 5, 360-362.

Waldeyer, W. (1891). Über einige neuere Forschungen im Gebiete der Anatomie des Centralnervensystems. Deutsche med. Wchnschr., 17, 1352-1356.

Wall, P. D. (1958). Excitability changes in afferent fibre terminations and their relation to slow potentials. J. Physiol., 142, 1-21.

Watanabe, A., and Grundfest, H. (1961). Impulse propagation at the septal and commissural junctions of crayfish lateral giant axons. J. Gen. Physiol., 45, 267-308.

Weber, E., and Weber, E. H. (1845). Experimenta, quibus probatur nervos vagos rotatione machinae galvano-magneticae irritatos, motum cordis retardare et adeo intercipere. Ann. Univ. Med., Milano, 20, 227-228.

Weber, H. (1904). Über Anästhesie durch Adrenalin. Verhandl. deutsch. Gesellsch. inn. Med., 21, 616-619.

Weidmann, H., and Cerletti, A. (1957). Die Wirkung von D-Lysergsäure-diäthylamid und 5-Hydroxytryptamin (Serotonin) auf spinale Reflexe der Katze. Helvet. Physiol. Acta, 15, 376-383.

———, ——— (1960). Studies on Psilocybin and related compounds. I. Structure/activity relationship of oxyindole-derivatives with regard to their effect on the knee jerk of spinal cats. Helvet. Physiol. Acta, 18, 174-182.

Weil-Malherbe, H., Axelrod, J., and Tomchick, R. (1959). Blood-brain barrier for adrenaline. Science, 129, 1226-1227.

Weil-Malherbe, H., Whitby, L. G., and Axelrod, J. (1961). The uptake of circulating [3H] norepinephrine by the pituitary gland and various areas of the brain. J. Neurochem., 8, 55-64.

Welsh, J. H. (1939a). Chemical mediation in crustaceans. I. The occurrence of acetylcholine in nervous tissues and its action on the decapod heart. J. Exper. Biol., 16, 198-219.

——— (1939b). Chemical mediation in crustaceans. II. The action of acetylcholine and adrenaline on the isolated heart of Panulirus argus. Physiol. Zoö., 12, 231-237.

——— (1953). Excitation of the heart of Venus mercenaria. Arch. exper. Path. u. Pharmakol., 219, 23-29.

——— (1957). Serotonin as a possible neurohumoral agent: evidence obtained in lower animals. Ann. N.Y. Acad. Sc., 66, 618-630.

Welsh, J. H., and Moorhead, M. (1959). Identification and assay of 5-hydroxytryptamine in molluscan tissues by fluorescence method. Science, 129, 1491-1492.

Werle, E., and Palm, D. (1950). Histamin in Nerven. II. Biochem. Ztschr., 320, 322-334.

Werner, G. (1961). Antidromic activity in motor nerves and its relation to a generator event in nerve terminals. J. Neurophysiol., 24, 401-413.

West, G. B. (1957). Histamine in nervous tissue, in: *Metabolism of the Nervous System* (D. Richter, ed.). Oxford, Pergamon Press, pp. 578-581.

White, T. (1960). Formation and catabolism of histamine in cat brain *in vivo*. J. Physiol., *152*, 299-308.

Whittaker, V. P. (1959). The isolation and characterization of acetylcholine-containing particles from brain. Biochem. J., *72*, 694-706.

Wiersma, C. A. G. (1947). Giant nerve fibre system of the crayfish. A contribution to comparative physiology of synapse. J. Neurophysiol., *10*, 23-38.

Wilson, I. B., and Nachmansohn, D. (1954). The generation of bioelectric potentials, in: *Ion Transport Across Membranes* (H. T. Clarke, ed.). New York, Academic Press, pp. 35-64.

Wilson, V. J. (1959). Recurrent facilitation of spinal reflexes. J. Gen. Physiol., *42*, 703-713.

Wilson, V. J., and Burgess, P. R. (1961). Changes in the membrane during recurrent disinhibition of spinal motoneurons. Nature, *191*, 918-919.

—, — (1962). Disinhibition in the cat spinal cord. J. Neurophysiol., *25*, 392-404.

Wilson, V. J., Diecke, F. P. J., and Talbot, W. H. (1960). Action of tetanus toxin on conditioning of spinal motoneurons. J. Neurophysiol., *23*, 659-666.

Witanowski, W. R. (1925). Über humorale Übertragbarkeit der Herznervenwirkung. VIII. Mitteilung. Pflügers Arch. ges. Physiol., *208*, 694-704.

Witzleb, E. (1959). Zur Frage von cholinergischen Mechanismen bei der Erregung von afferenten Systemen. Pflügers Arch. ges. Physiol., *269*, 439-470.

Woodbury, J. W., and Patton, H. D. (1952). Electrical activity of single spinal cord elements. Cold Spr. Harb. Symp. quant. biol., *17*, 185-188.

Woolley, D. W. (1957). Serotonin in mental disorders, in: *Hormones, Brain Function and Behavior* (H. Hoagland, ed.). New York, Academic Press, pp. 127-140.

Wundt, W. M. (1871). Untersuchungen zur Mechanik der Nerven und Nervencentren, Abth. 2. Über den Reflexvorgang und das Wesen der centralen Innervation., Erlangen, F. Enke.

Wybauw, L. (1936). Transmission humorale de la vaso-dilatation provoquée par l'excitation du bout périphérique des racines postérieurs lombaires chez le chat. C.R. Soc. Biol., Paris, *123*, 524-528.

Wyckoff, R. W. G., and Young, J. Z. (1956). The motoneuron surface. Proc. Roy. Soc. London B:*144*, 440-450.

Yamamoto, T. (1960). Electron microscopic investigation on the relationship between the smooth muscle cell of the Proc. vermiformis and the autonomic peripheral nerves. Acta neuroveg., *21*, 406-425.

Young, J. Z. (1939). Fused neurons and synaptic contacts in the giant nerve fibres of cephalopods. Phil. Tr., B:*229*, 465-503.

Zeller, E. A. (1959). The role of amine oxidases in the destruction of catecholamines. Pharmacol. Rev., *11*, 387-393.

Zetler, G. (1956). Substanz P, ein Polypeptid aus Darm und Gehirn mit depressiven, hyperalgetischen und Morphin-antagonistischen Wirkungen auf das Zentralnervensystem. Arch. exper. Path. u. Pharmakol., *228*, 513-538.

—— (1960). Pharmacological actions of substance P on the central nervous system, in: *Polypeptides Which Affect Smooth Muscles and Blood Vessels* (M. Schachter, ed.). Oxford, Pergamon Press, pp. 179-191.

—— (1961). Zwei neue pharmakologisch aktive Polypeptide in einem Substanz P-haltigen Hirnextrakt. Arch. exper. Path. u. Pharmakol., *242*, 330-352.

Zetler, G., and Schlosser, L. (1955). Über die Verteilung von Substanz P und Cholinacetylase im Gehirn. Arch. exper. Path. u. Pharmakol., *224*, 150-175.

AUTHOR INDEX

123

SUBJECT INDEX